CONTENTS

ISBN 0-8497-6258-8

Unit 1

Time Signatures and Rhythm

Time Signatures

The **time signature** is the two numbers written at the beginning of a piece.

- The top number tells how many beats are in each measure.
- The bottom number tells what kind of note gets one beat.

In a time signature with a **4** on the bottom, the **quarter note** ♩ gets one beat.

In a time signature with an **8** on the bottom, the **eighth note** ♪ gets one beat.

1. Tell how many beats in each measure for these time signatures.

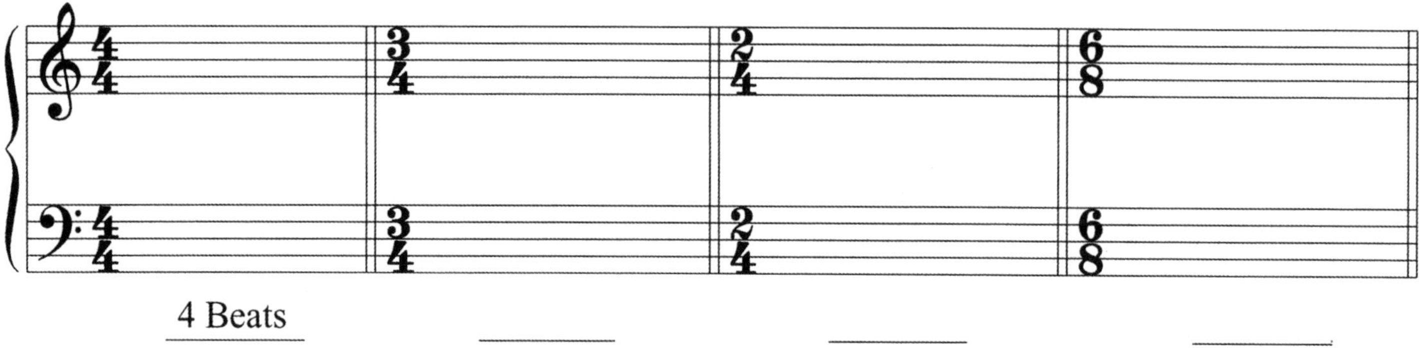

4 Beats ________ ________ ________

2. What kind of note will get one beat in $\frac{4}{4}$? ______________

3. What kind of note will get one beat in $\frac{6}{8}$? ______________

4. Write in the counts for these rhythms. Play and count aloud.

From *Old French Song* by Tchaikovsky

From *Écossaise* by Beethoven

* Use a + sign for the word "and".

From *Le Petit Rien* by Couperin

From *Song* by Kabalevsky

From *Romance* by Czerny

5. Write the correct time signature for each example.
   Write in the counts. Play and count aloud.

From *Arabesque* by Burgmüller

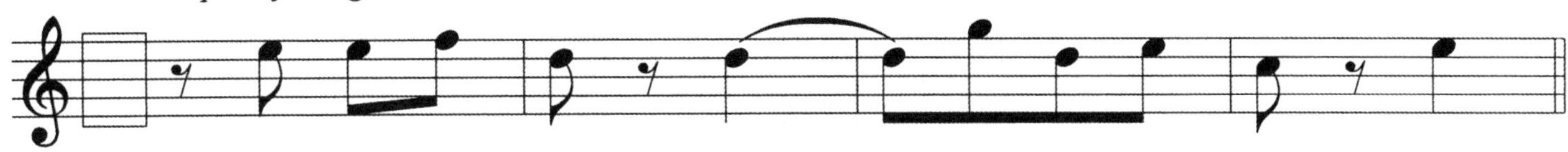

From *Minuet* by Handel

From *Wild Horseman* by Schumann

From *Sonatina* by Biehl

Sixteenth Notes

One sixteenth note has two flags.

Two or more sixteenth notes are connected with a double beam.

Four sixteenth notes equal one quarter note. 

One sixteenth rest:

7. Clap and count these rhythms.

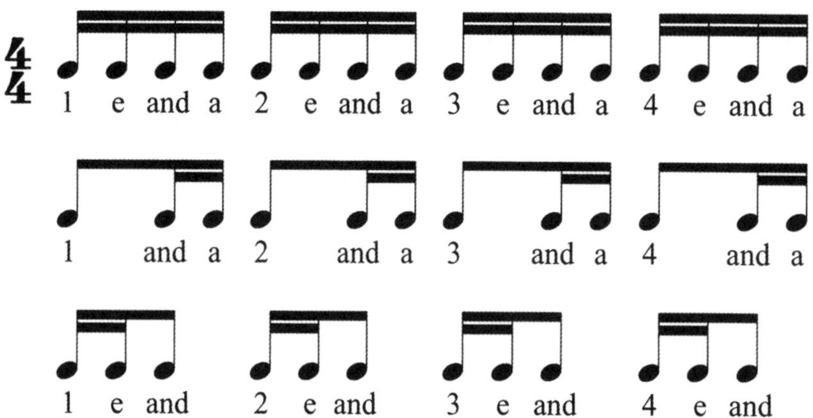

Dotted Eighth Note Rhythms

The dotted eighth note is often followed by one sixteenth note.

The dotted eighth note is equal to three sixteenth notes.
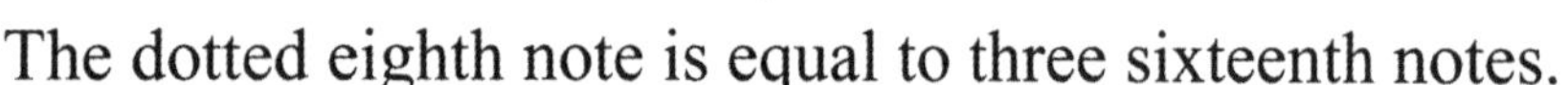

The dot adds half of the value of the note.

8. Clap and count this rhythm.

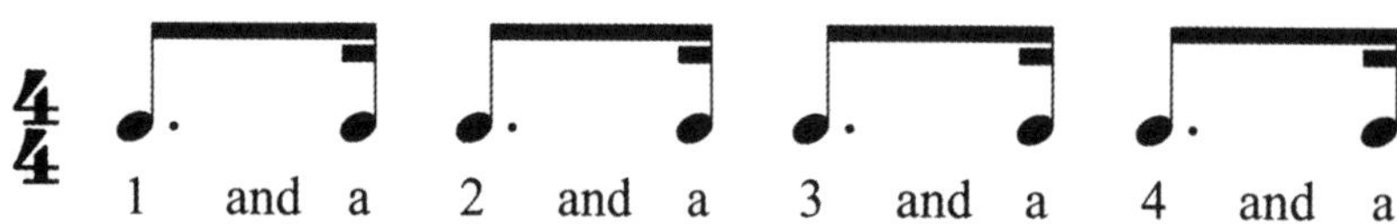

9. Write in the counts. Clap and count aloud.

10. Write in the counts for these rhythms. Play and count aloud.

11. Write sixteenth notes to equal each of the following notes.

12. Write sixteenth notes to complete each measure. Clap and count the rhythms.

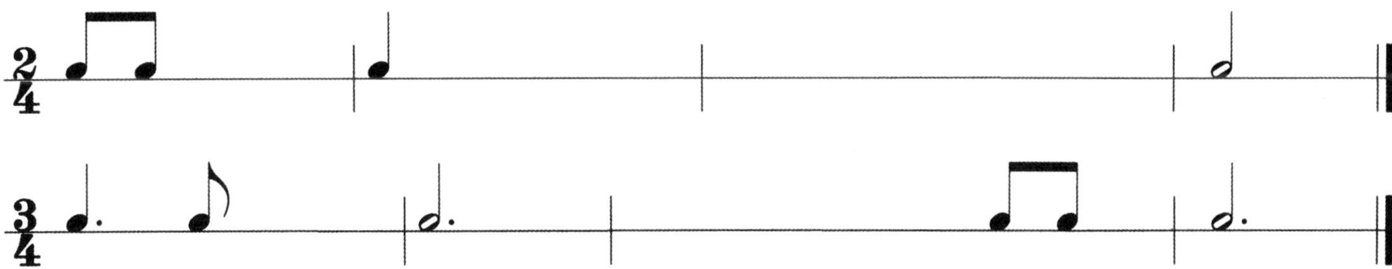

Triplet

The word **triplet** means three.

The eighth note triplet is equal to one quarter note.

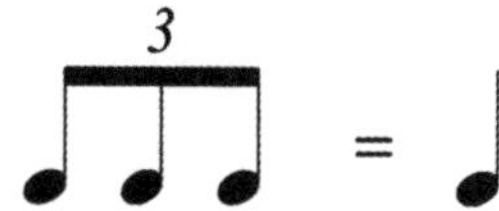

6. Write in the counts for these rhythms. Play and count aloud.

From *Minuet* by Telemann

From *Minuet* by Telemann

From *Minuet* by Bach

From *Sonatina Op. 36 No. 1* by Clementi

From *Minuet* by Mozart

Time Signature $\frac{2}{2}$ (¢)

2 means two beats in each measure.
2 means the half note gets one beat.

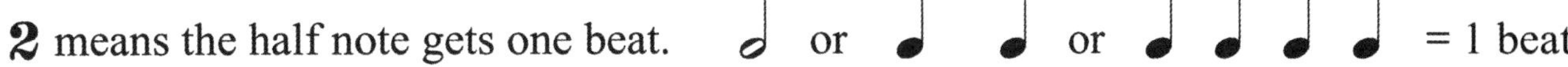

The time signature $\frac{2}{2}$ is usually written with the sign ¢ .
It means *alla breve* or "cut time ".

Clap and count this rhythm aloud:

13. Write in the counts for these musical examples. Play and count aloud.

From *Sonatina, Op. 36, No. 1* by Clementi

From *Musette* by Bach

Playing Music in $\frac{6}{8}$

A measure in $\frac{6}{8}$ can be divided in half, creating a feeling of two pulses per measure.

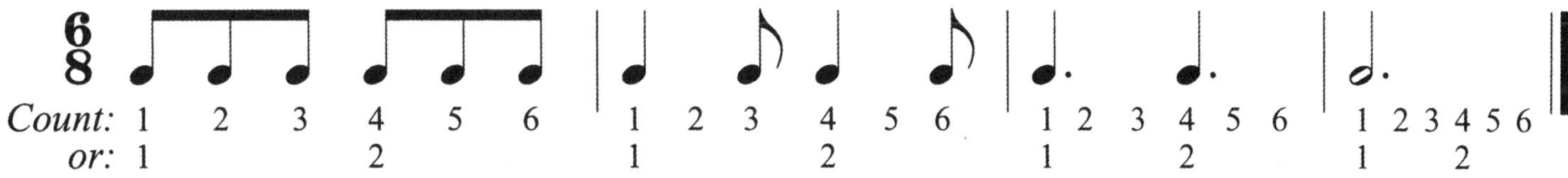

14. First, play and count 6 beats in each measure. Play again and count two pulses per measure.

From *Romance* by Czerny

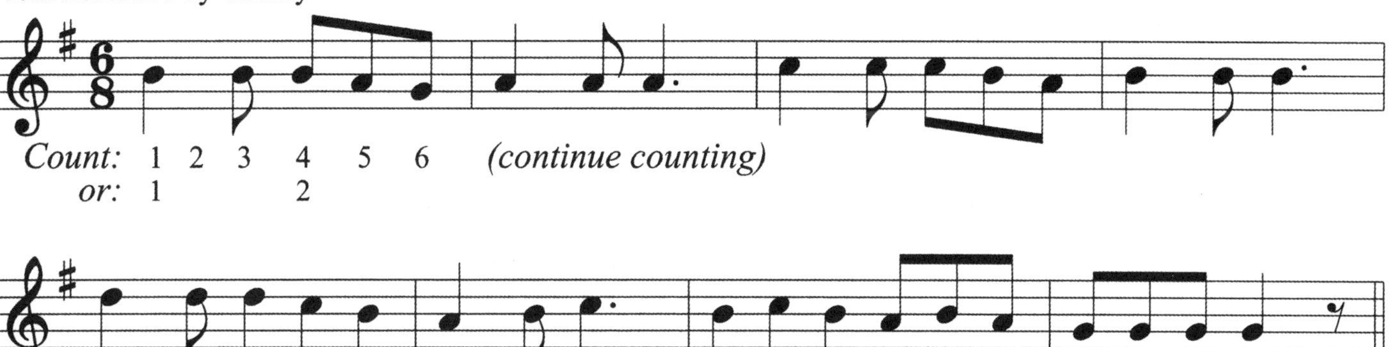

Unit 2
Major Key Signatures

The Order of Sharps

The sharps are always written in the same order on the staff. Memorize the order of sharps.

1. Write the order of sharps three times in treble and bass staff.

Naming Major Sharp Key Signatures

To discover the name of a Major sharp key:

- Name the last sharp to the right in the key signature.

- Name the next letter up in the music alphabet (go up a half step). This is the name of the Major sharp key.

Reminder: The key of C Major has no sharps or flats in the key signature.

2. Write the names of these Major key signatures.

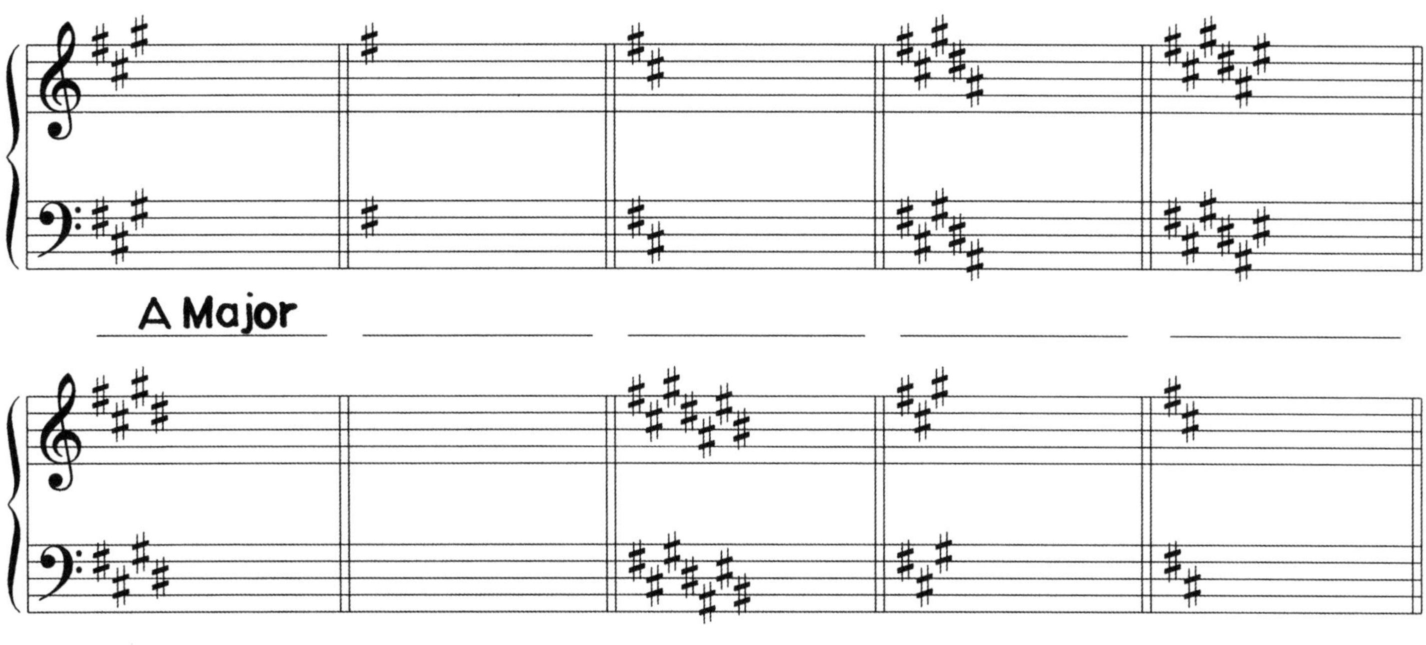

Writing Major Sharp Key Signatures

To write the key signature for a Major sharp key:

- Name the note one half step below the key note.
- Write the order of sharps up to and including the sharp that is one half step below the key note.

3. Write these Major key signatures in treble and bass staff.

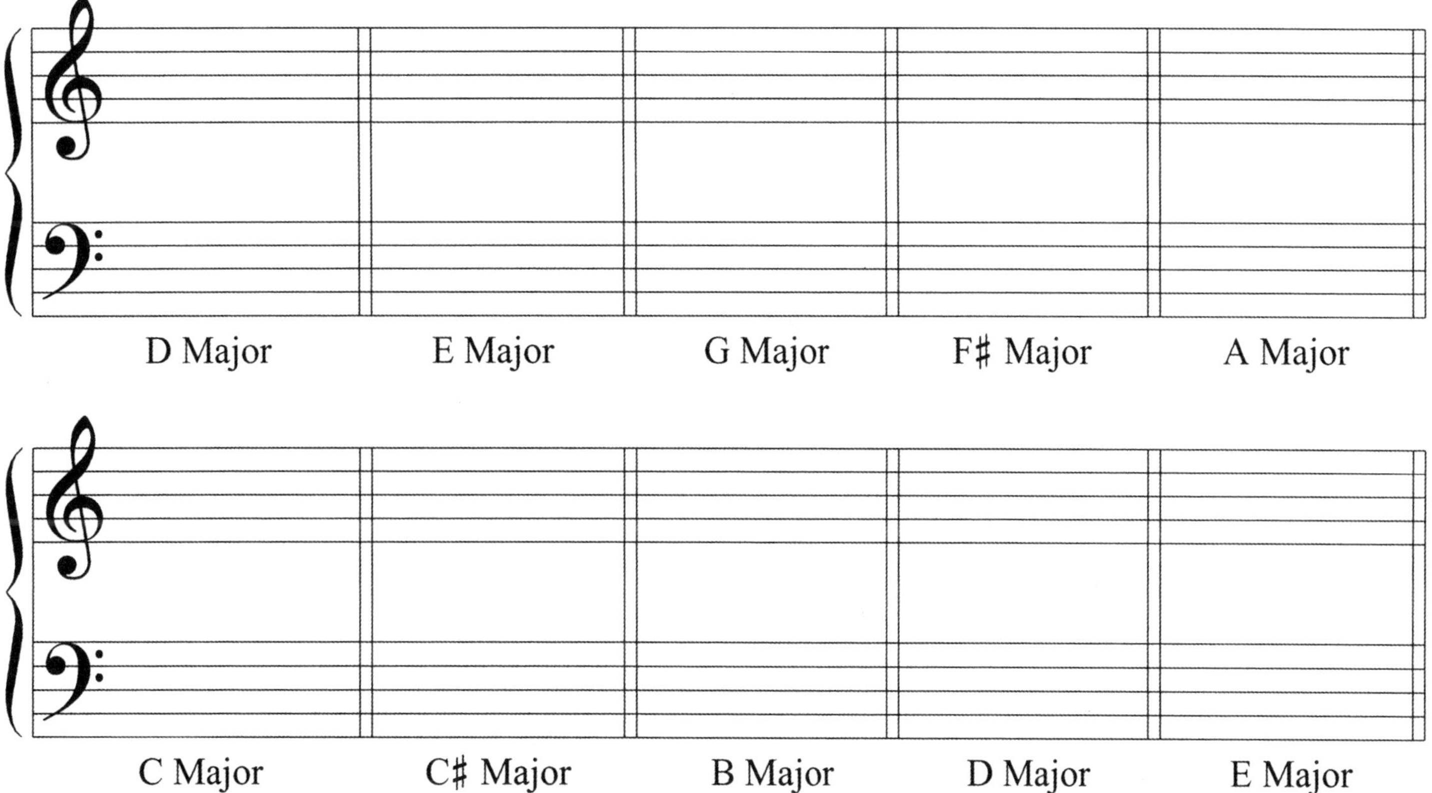

The Order of Flats

The flats are always written in the same order on the staff. Memorize the order of flats.

4. Write the order of flats three times in treble and bass staff.

Naming Major Flat Key Signatures

To discover the name of a Major flat key:

- Name the next to last flat in the key signature.
- The letter name of the flat is the name of the Major key.

Exception: The key of F Major has only one flat, B♭.

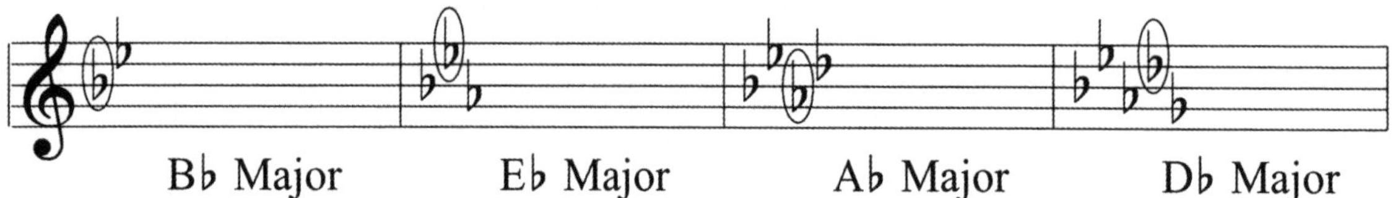

5. Write the names of these Major key signatures.

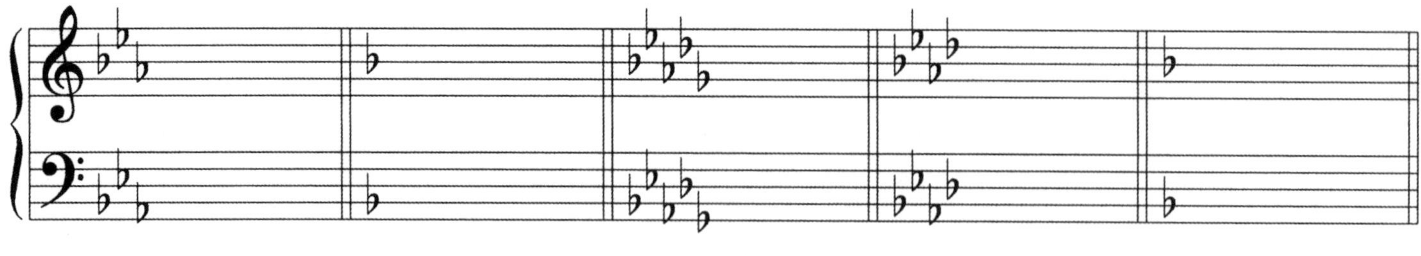

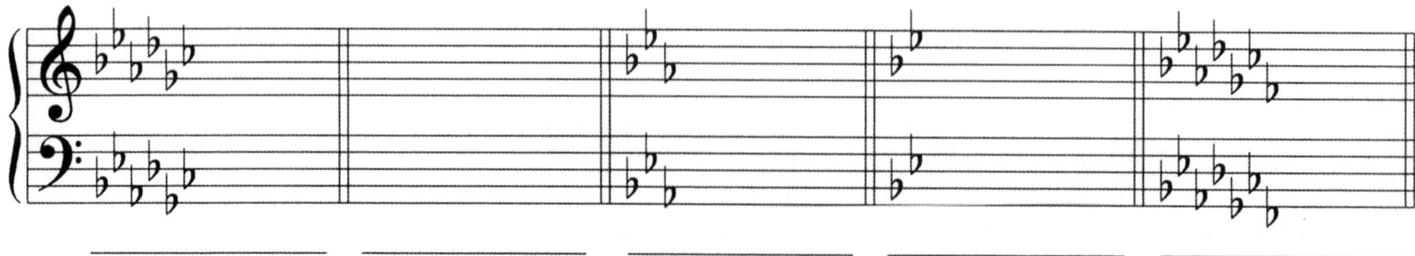

Writing Major Flat Key Signatures

To write a Major flat key signature, write the order of flats up to and including the flat **after** the key note. (*Exception:* The Key of F Major only has one flat, B♭.)

Example: Key of **A♭ Major**: B E **A** D

6. Write these Major key signatures in treble and bass staff.

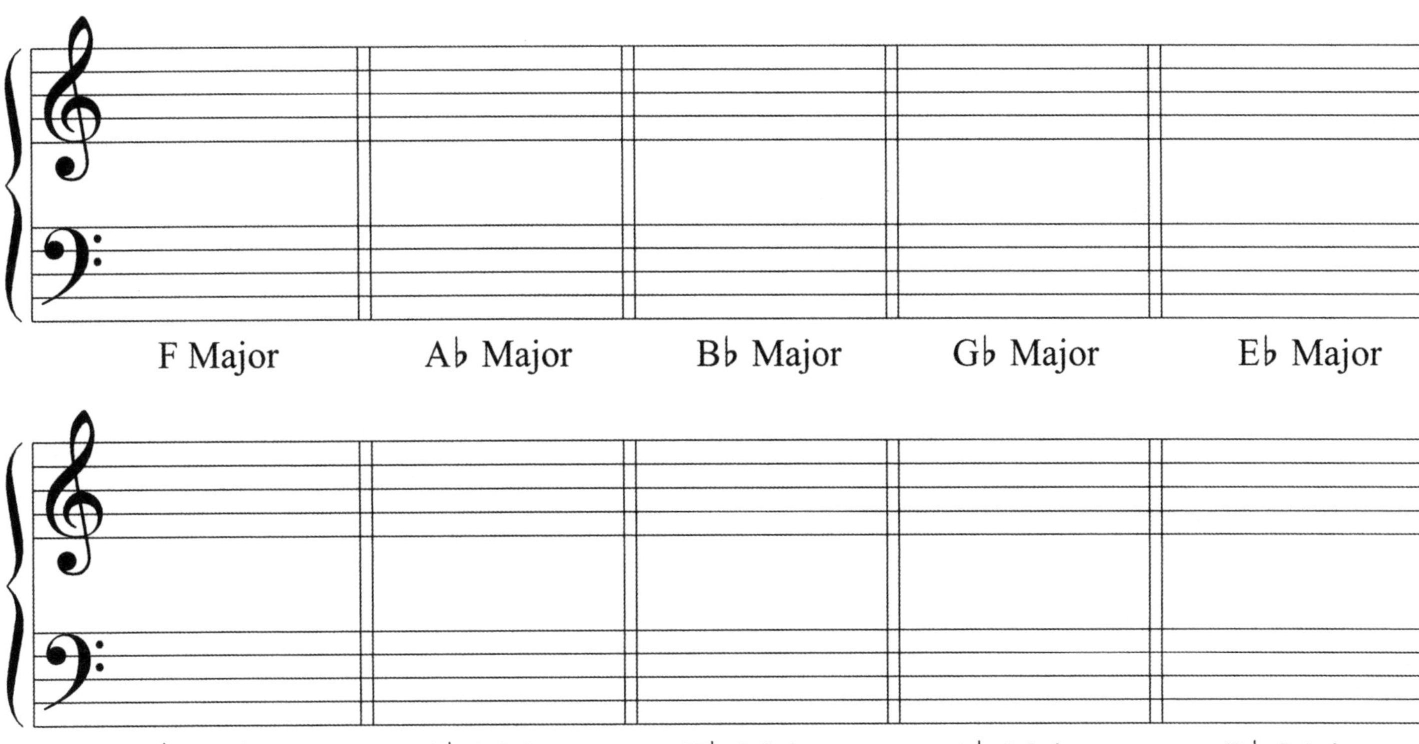

Key Signature Review

7. Write the names of these Major key signatures.

Major Sharp Scales and Key Signatures

8. Add the correct sharps to form each Major scale, then write the key signature.

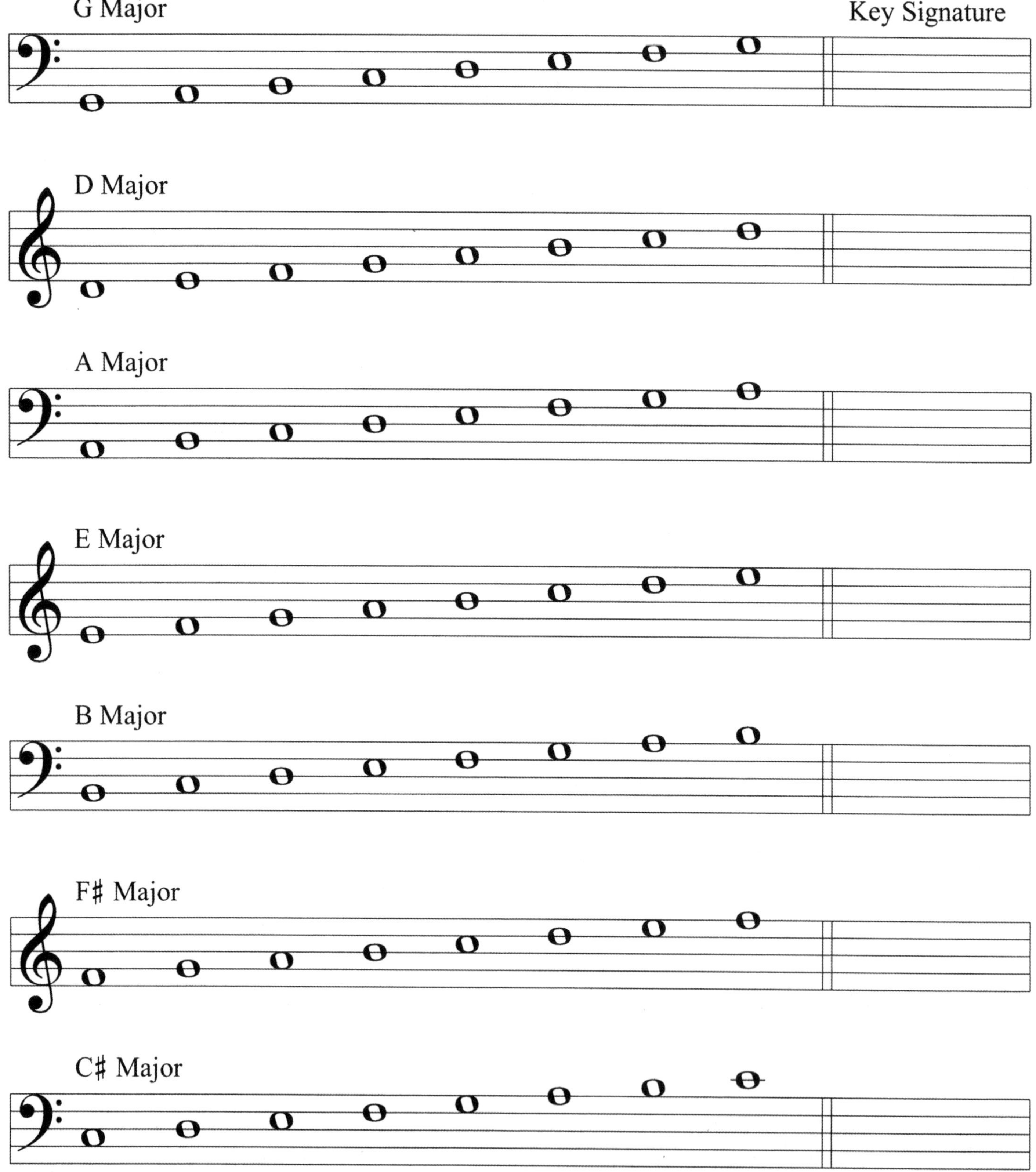

Major Flat Scales and Key Signatures

9. Add the correct flats to form each Major scale, then write the key signature.

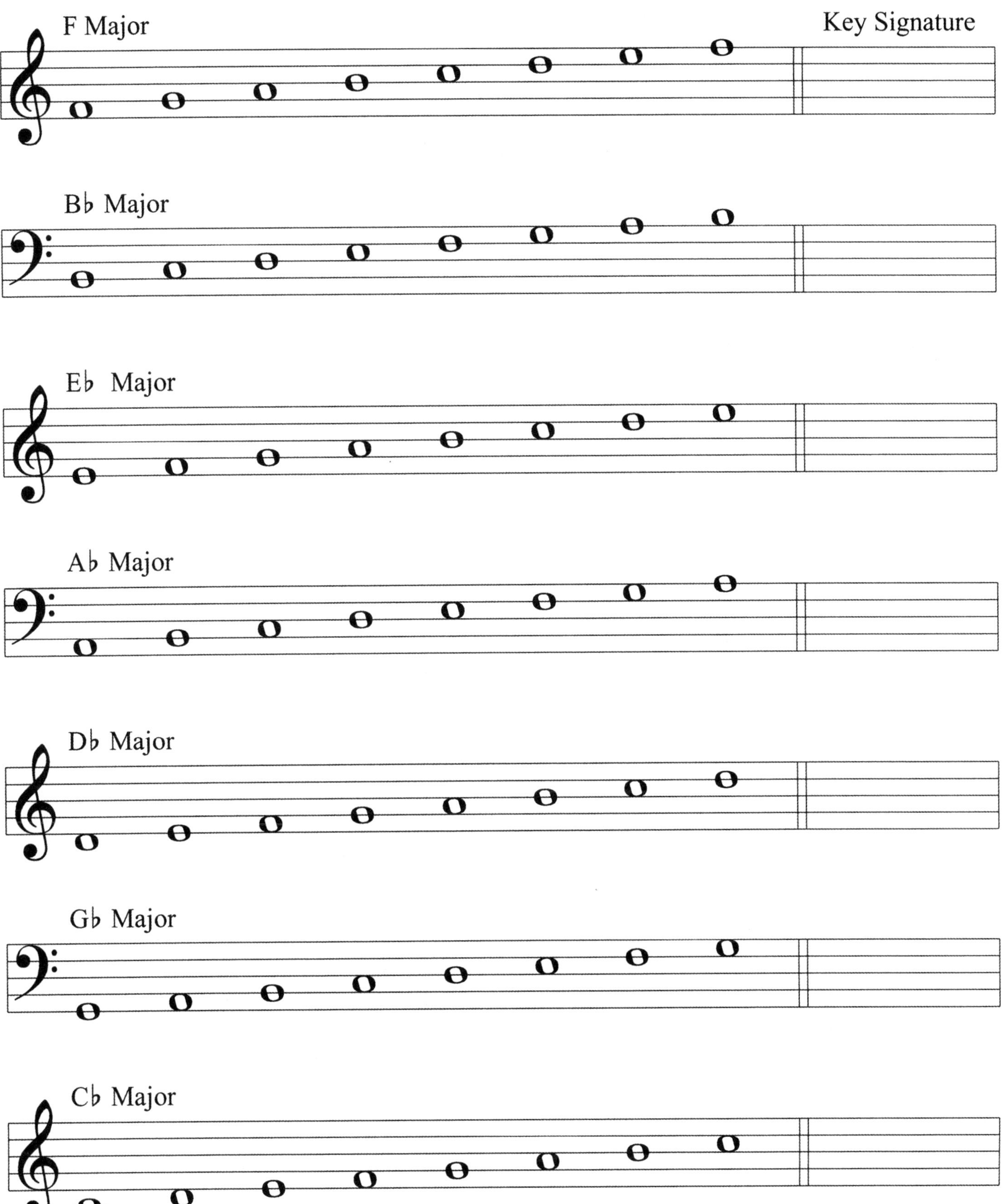

Unit 3

Minor Key Signatures

The same key signature is used for **relative** Major and minor keys.
The minor key is found **three half steps below** the Major key.

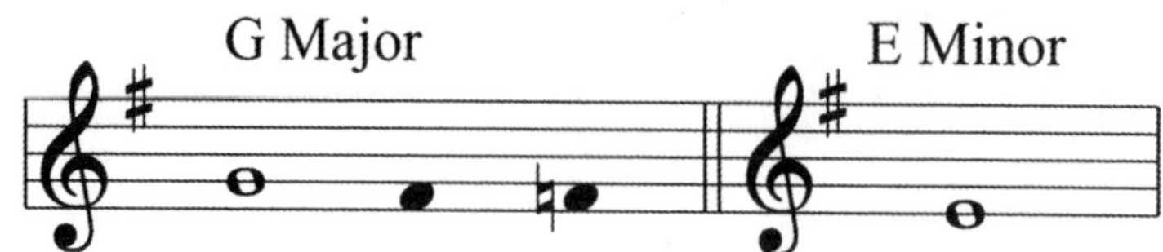

1. Write the names of these Major and minor key signatures.
   Find the relative minor key by counting three half steps down from the Major key.

______ Major ______ minor 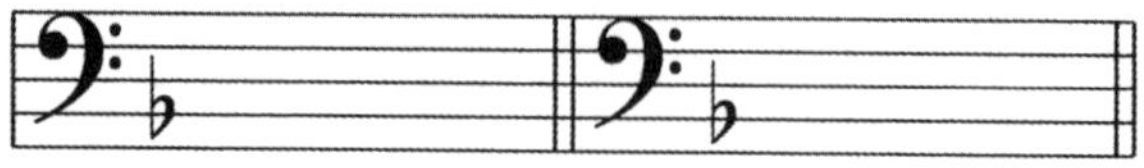 ______ Major ______ minor

______ Major ______ minor  ______ Major ______ minor

______ Major ______ minor 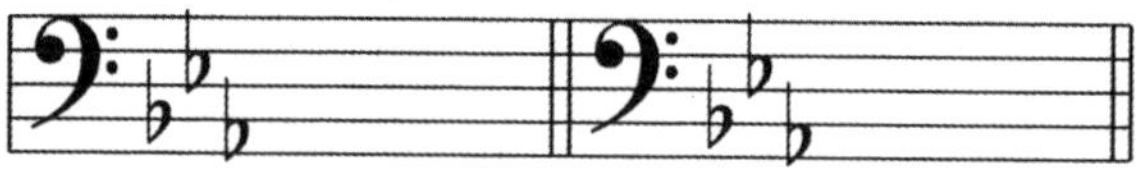 ______ Major ______ minor

______ Major ______ minor 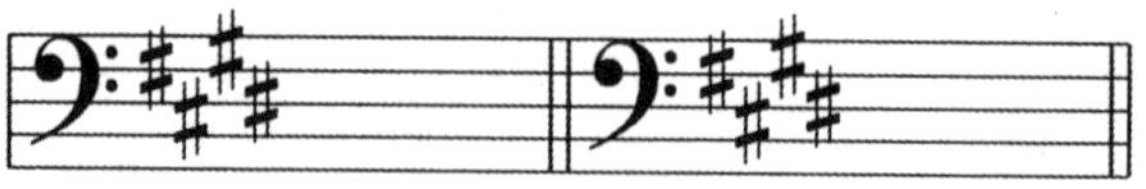 ______ Major ______ minor

______ Major ______ minor  ______ Major ______ minor

______ Major ______ minor 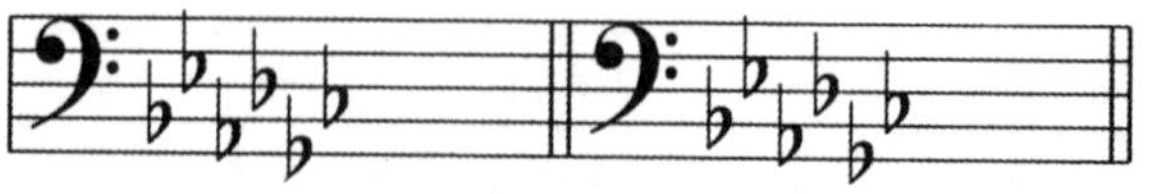 ______ Major ______ minor

2. Write these minor key signatures in treble and bass staff.

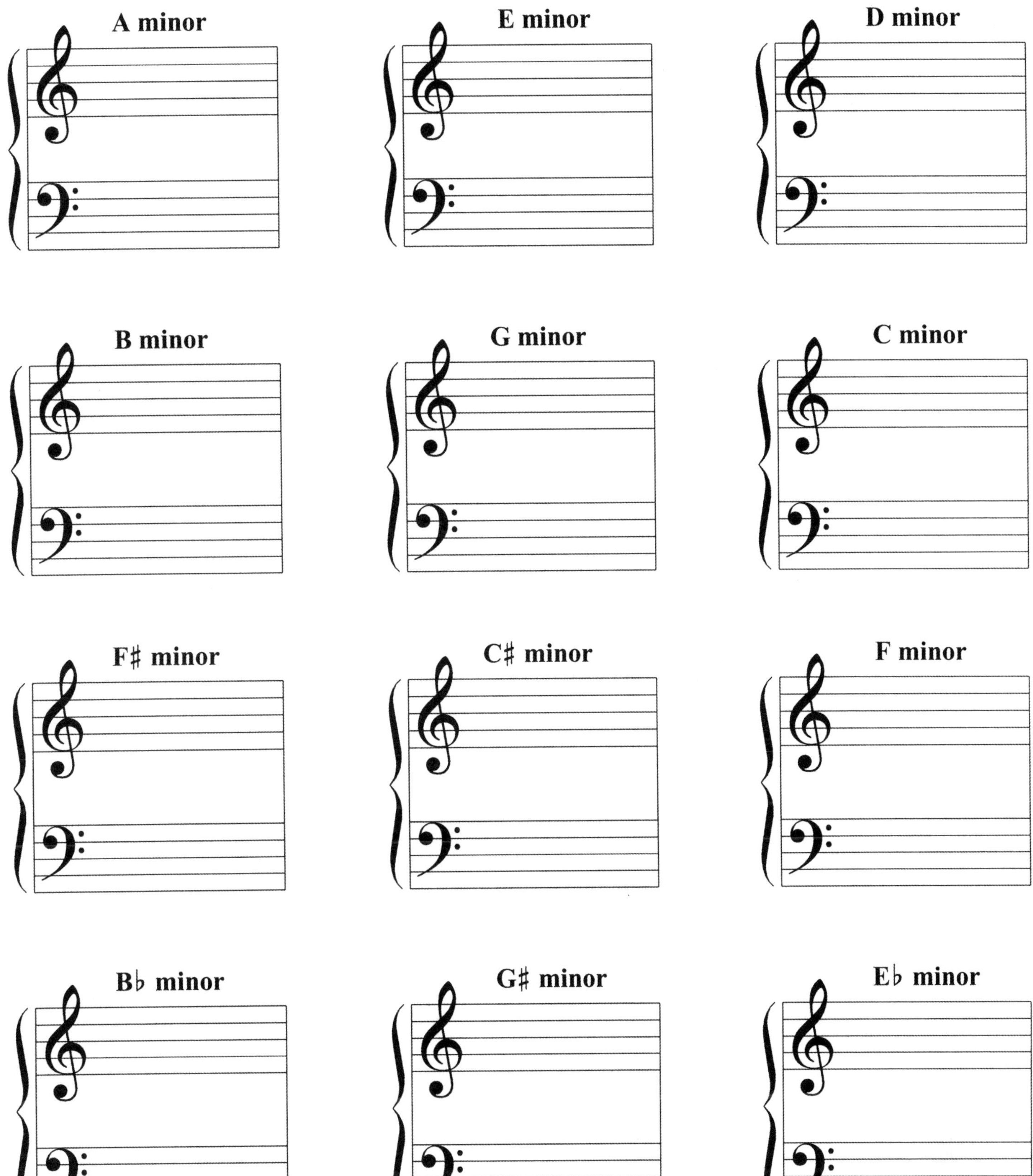

Unit 4

Minor Scales

Major and Relative Minor Scales

Each Major scale has a **relative minor** scale with the same key signature. The 6th note of the Major scale is the 1st note of the minor scale.

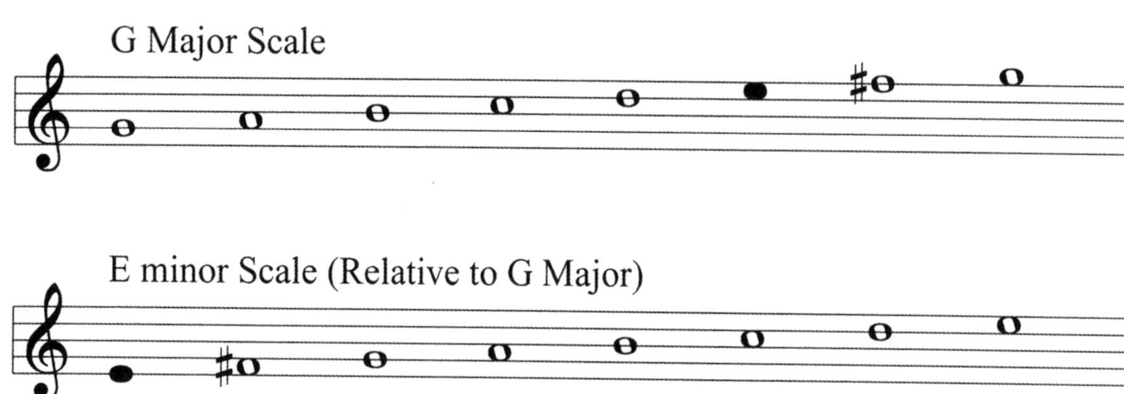

1. Draw each Major and relative minor scale.

C Major Scale

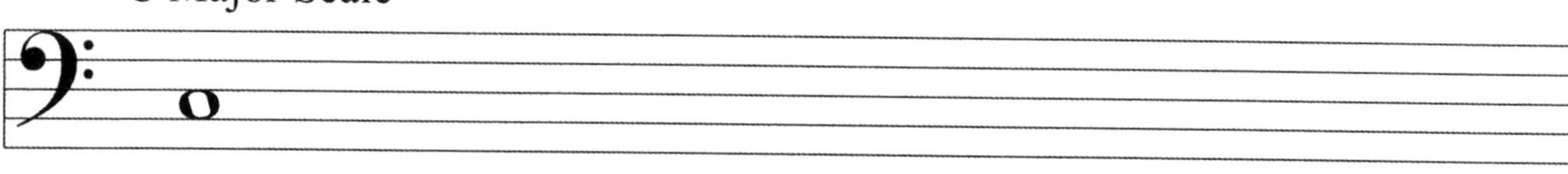

A minor Scale (Relative to C Major)

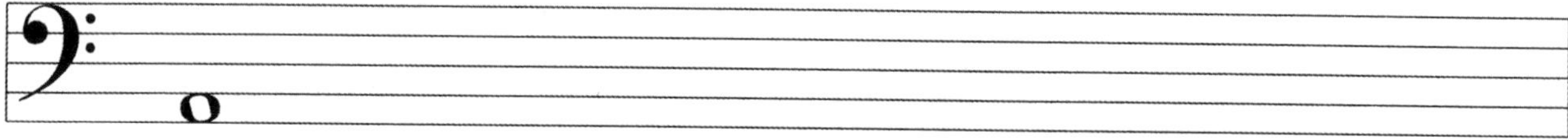

G Major Scale

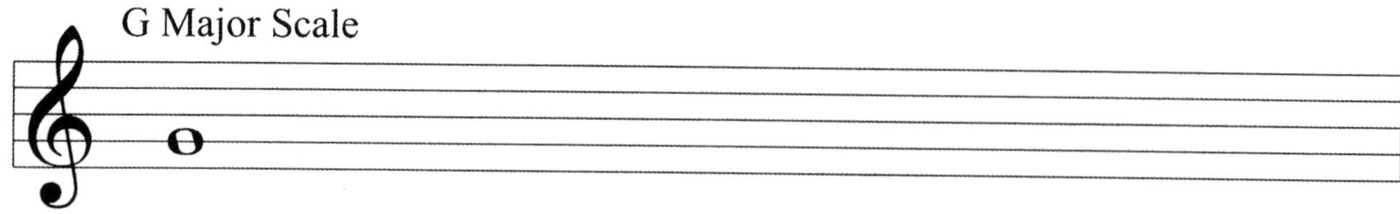

E minor Scale (Relative to G Major)

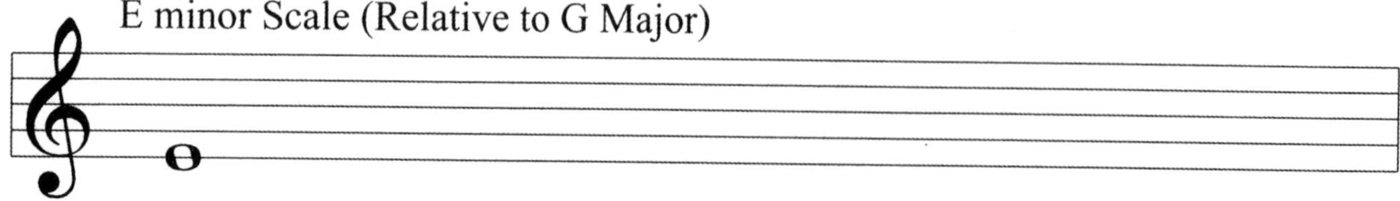

D Major Scale

B minor Scale (Relative to D Major)

F Major Scale

D minor Scale (Relative to F Major)

B♭ Major Scale

G minor Scale (Relative to B♭ Major)

E♭ Major Scale

C minor Scale (Relative to E♭ Major)

Forms of Minor Scales

There are three forms of minor scales: **natural, harmonic, melodic.**

Natural Minor Scale

The natural minor scale follows the key signature exactly.
None of the notes are changed.

Harmonic Minor Scale

The seventh note is raised one half step.

Melodic Minor Scale

The sixth and seventh notes are raised one half step going up and lowered going down.
The melodic minor scale going down uses the same notes as the natural minor scale.*

2. Change these Natural minor scales to Harmonic and Melodic minor scales by writing in the correct accidentals (observe the key signature).

E minor

Harmonic minor

Melodic minor

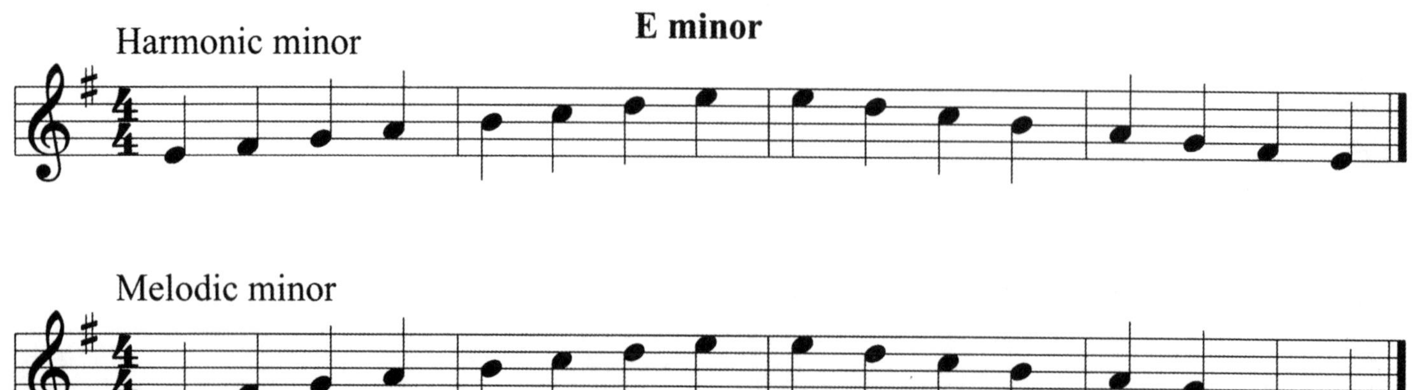

* Reminder: The bar line at the end of a measure cancels any accidentals.

D minor
Harmonic minor
Melodic minor
B minor
Harmonic minor
Melodic minor
G minor
Harmonic minor
Melodic minor
C minor
Harmonic minor
Melodic minor

Major and Minor Melodies

3. Three of these melodies are in Major keys, and three are in minor keys. Play each melody and determine if it is Major or minor. Name the key signature.

The Circle of Keys

The **circle of keys** is a diagram of all Major and minor key signatures. The sharp keys are arranged from the top, moving clockwise. The flat keys are arranged from the top, moving counterclockwise.

There are fifteen Major keys: seven sharp keys, seven flat keys, and one key with no sharps or flats. Likewise, there are fifteen relative minor keys.

The keys at the bottom of the circle are called **enharmonic** keys because their tones sound the same but are named and written differently.

The circle of keys is sometimes called the **circle of fifths** because the keys are arranged an interval of a fifth apart. Notice that as you move around the circle clockwise from the top, one new sharp is added to each key. As you move around the circle counterclockwise from the top, one new flat is added to each key.

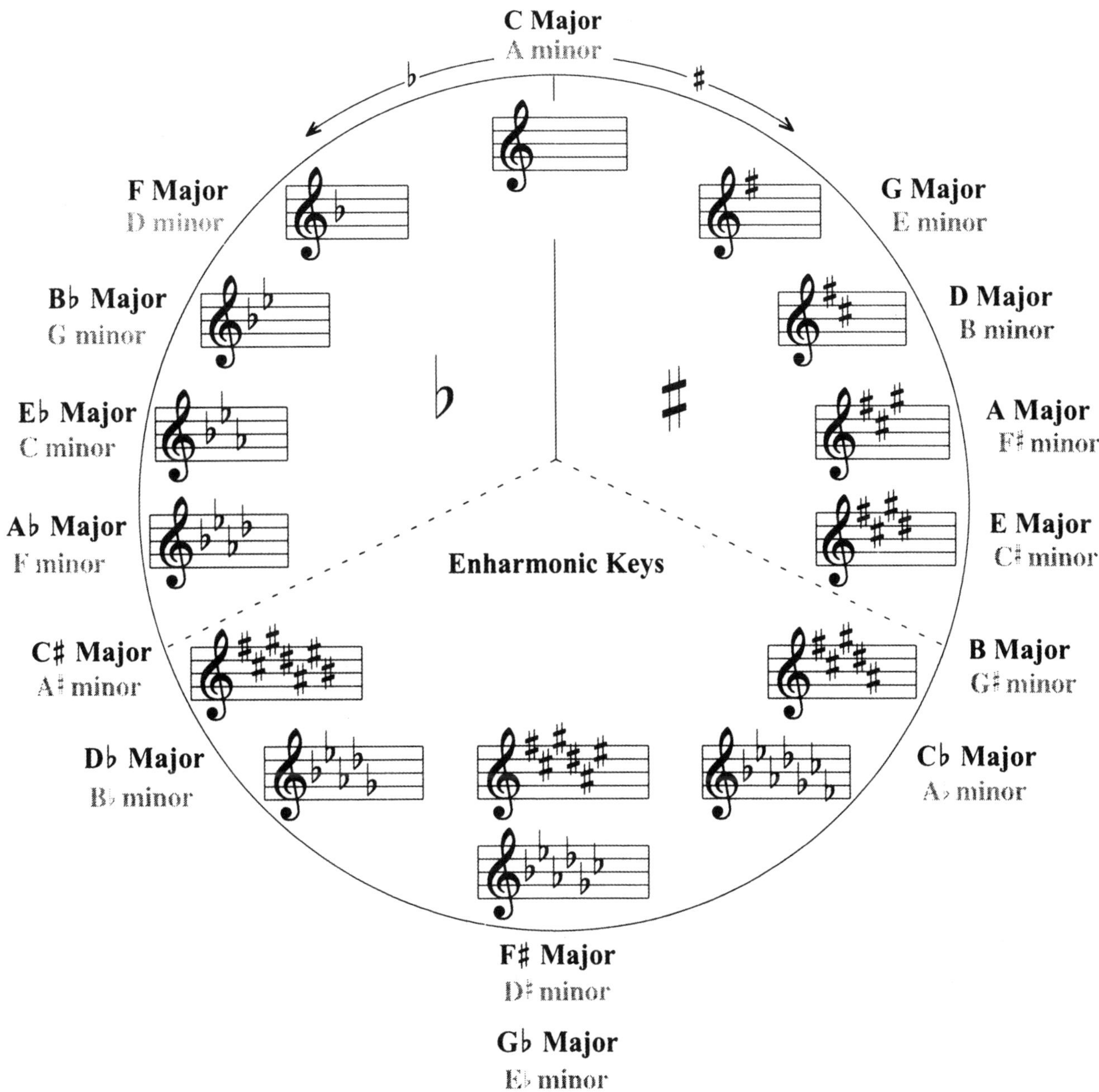

Unit 5

Intervals of the Scale

The intervals of the C Major scale are shown below. Each interval is formed from the tonic note of the scale.

- The 2nd, 3rd, 6th, and 7th are called **Major** intervals.
- The 4th, 5th, and octave are called **Perfect** intervals.

These intervals are the same for all Major scales.

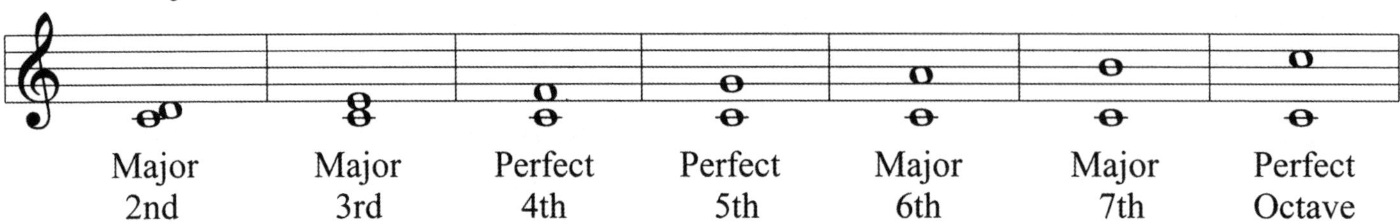

1. Draw a note above the one given to form harmonic intervals of the scale. Name each interval. Write **M** for Major and **P** for Perfect.

Key of ____________

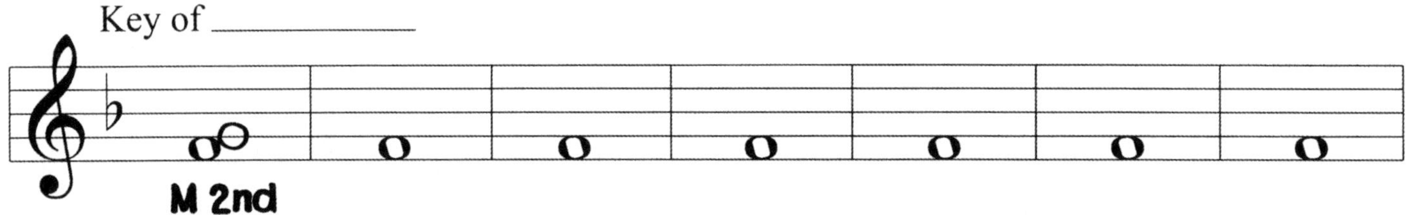

Key of ____________

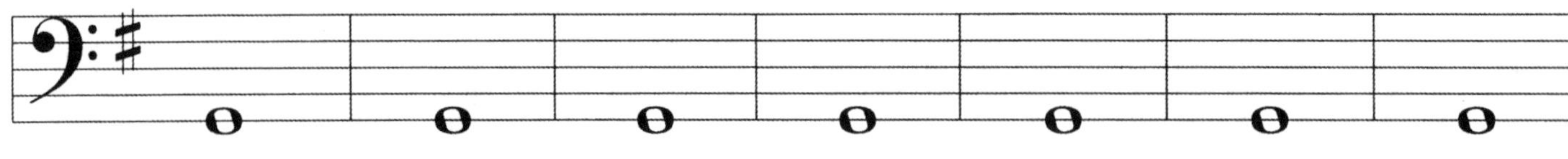

2. Name these harmonic intervals of the scale.

Key of ____________

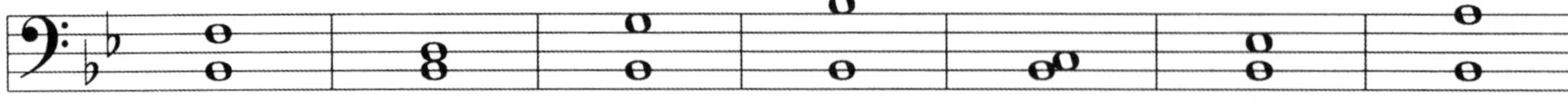

3. Name these melodic intervals of the scale.

Key of ____________

4. Identify these intervals. Think of the lowest note in each interval as the tonic note of a Major scale.

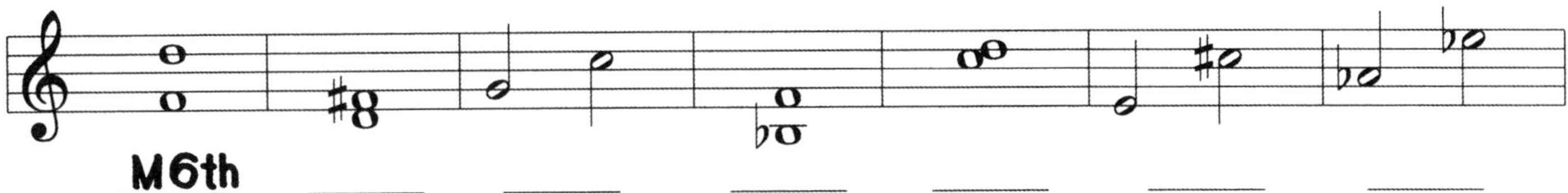

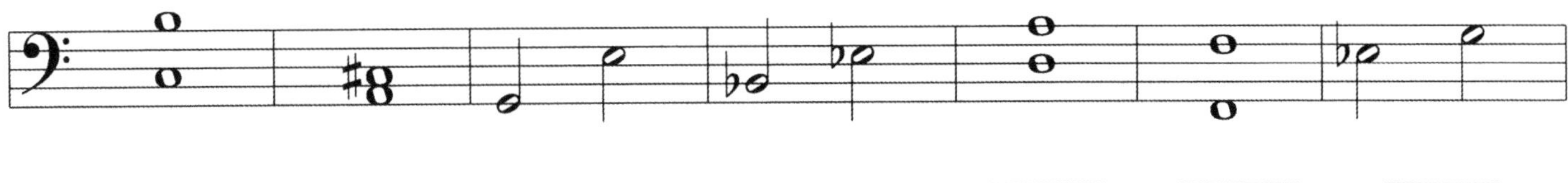

5. Draw a note above the one given to form these harmonic intervals.
Think of the Major scale to which each interval belongs and add the correct sharps or flats.

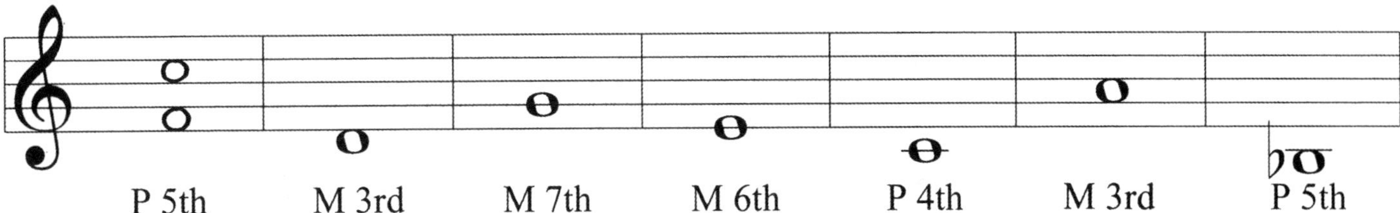

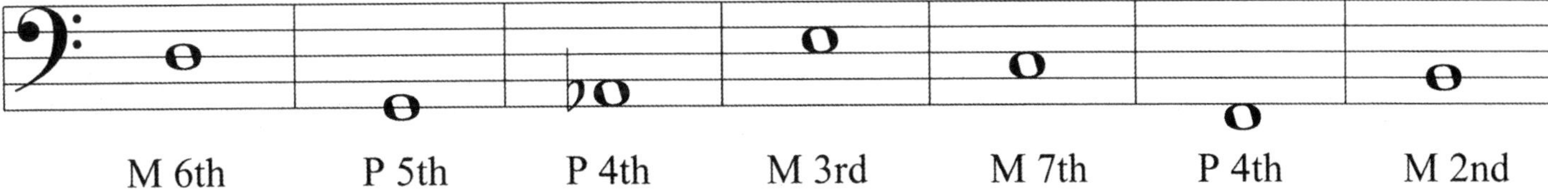

6. Name the circled intervals in the music below.

From *Minuet* by Handel

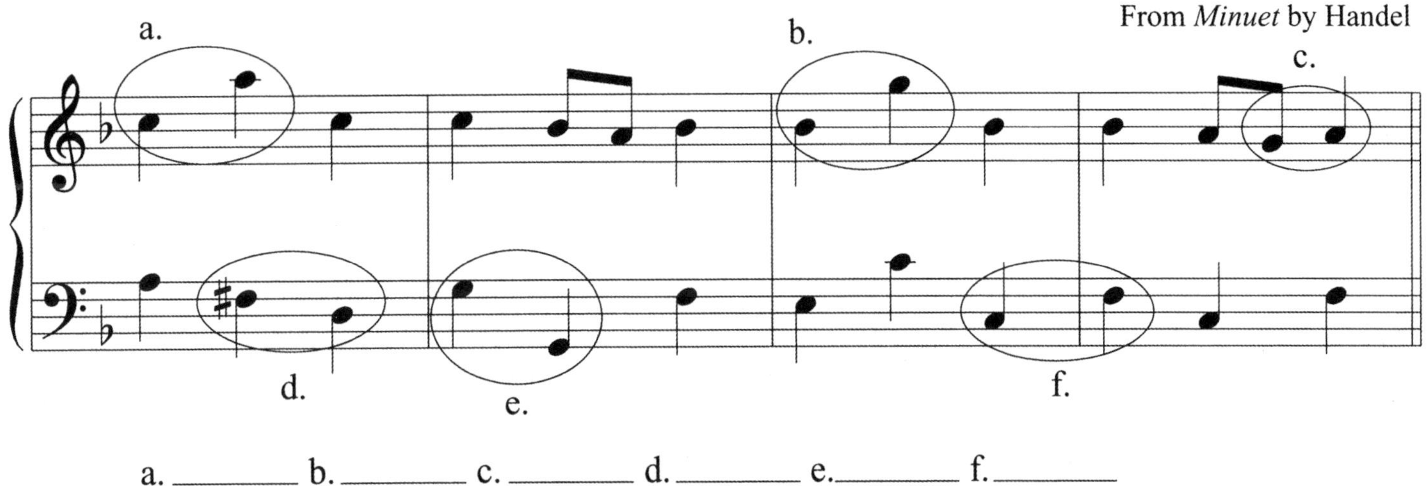

a. ________ b. ________ c. ________ d. ________ e. ________ f. ________

Unit 6
Triads

A **triad** is a three note chord. The notes of a triad are called the **root**, **3rd**, and **5th**. The root names the triad.

Major and minor Triads

The first, third and fifth notes of a Major scale form a **Major triad**.

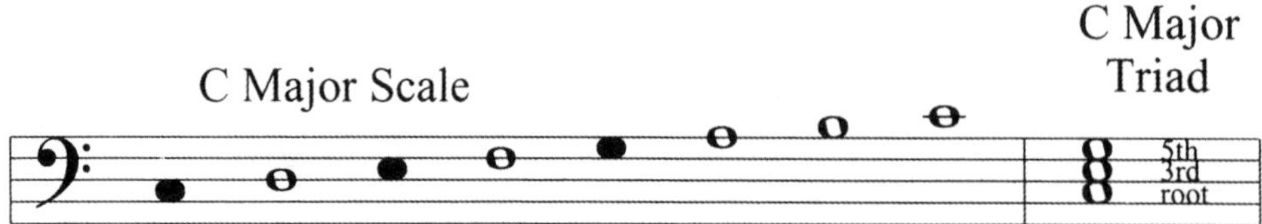

To change a Major triad into a **minor** triad, lower the 3rd one half step.

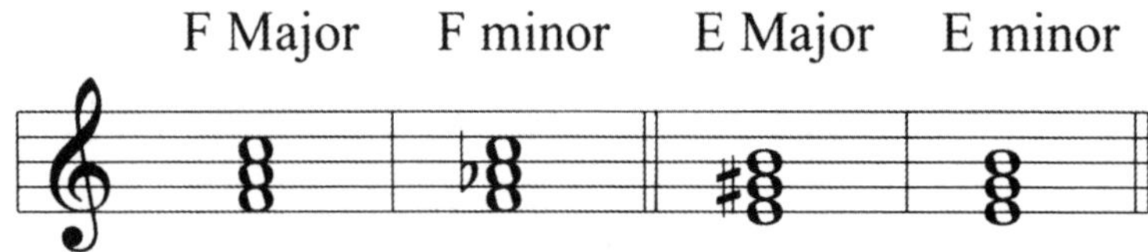

1. Name these Major and minor triads.

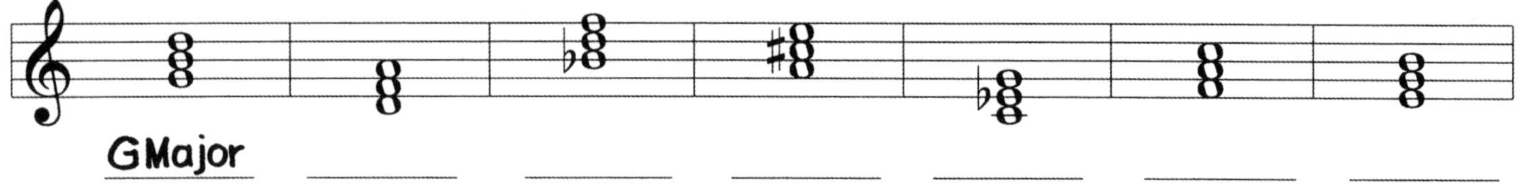

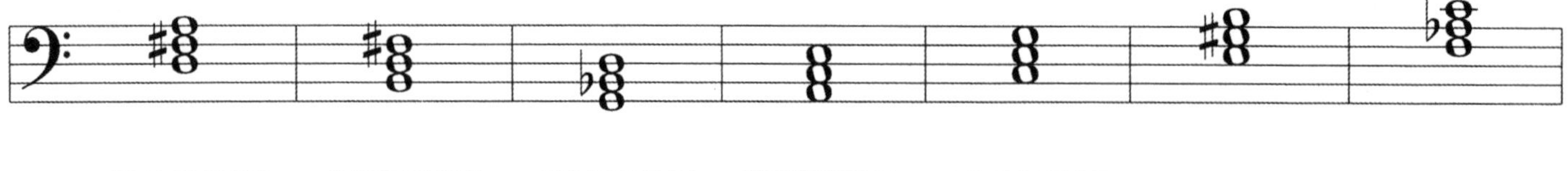

2. Draw these Major and minor triads.

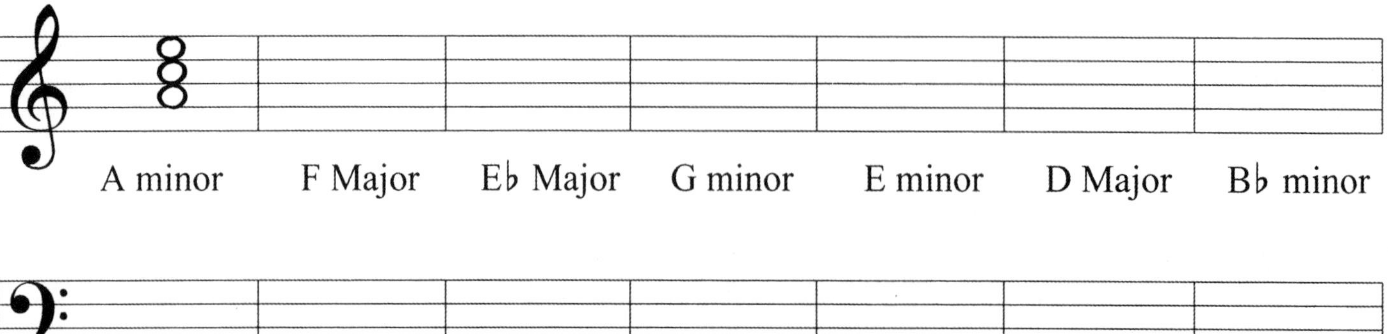

4. Name the circled triads in each musical example.

From *German Dance* by Haydn

From *Minuet* by Bach

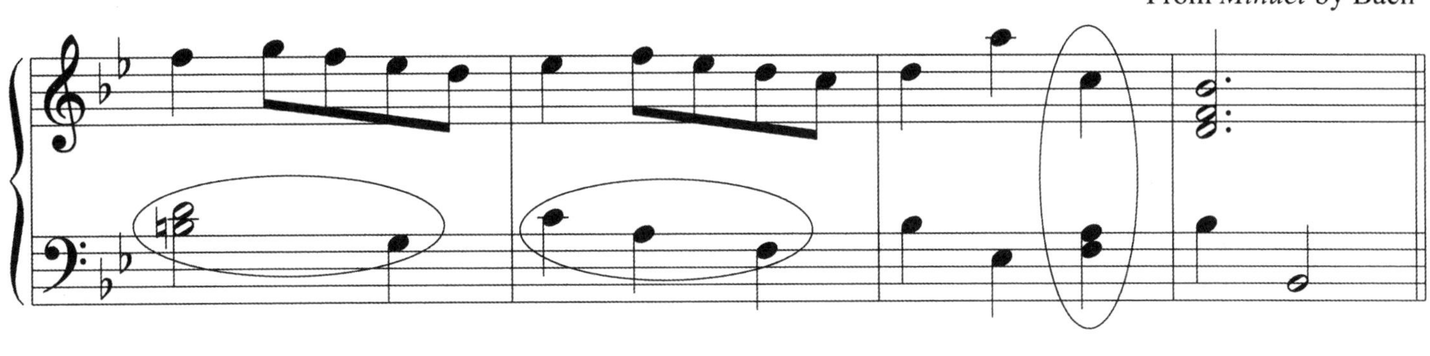

From *Minuet* by Handel

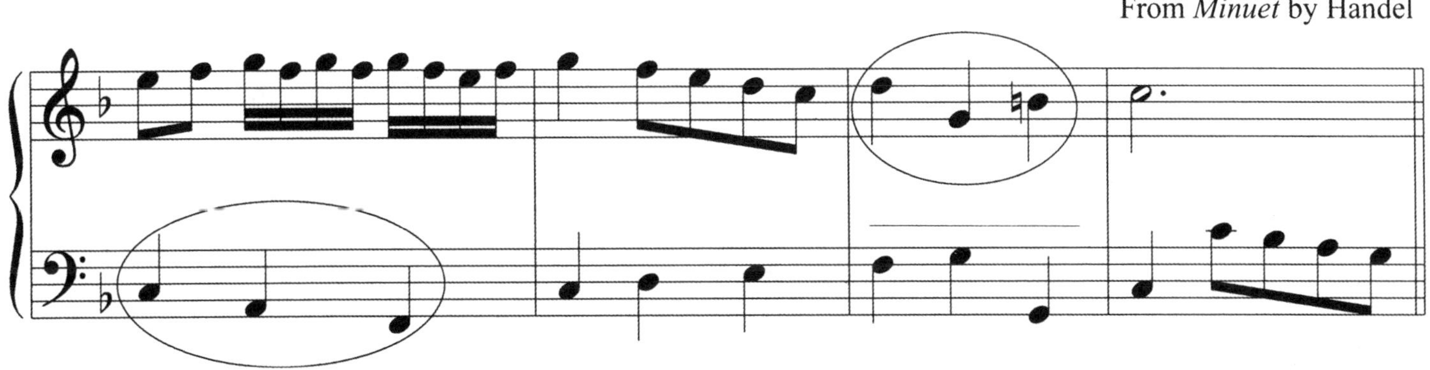

From *Waltz* by Kabalevsky

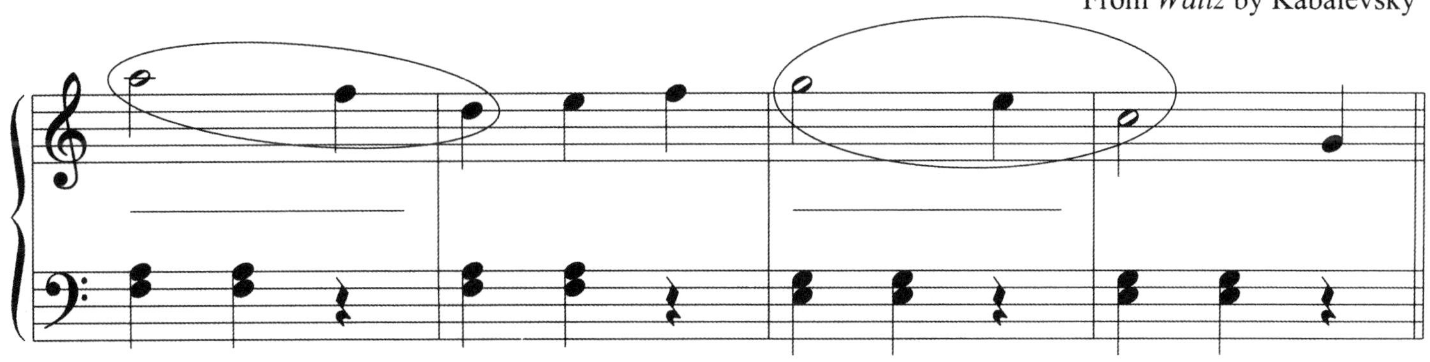

Augmented Triads

An **Augmented** triad is formed by raising the 5th of a Major triad one half step.

5. Draw an Augmented triad after each Major triad.

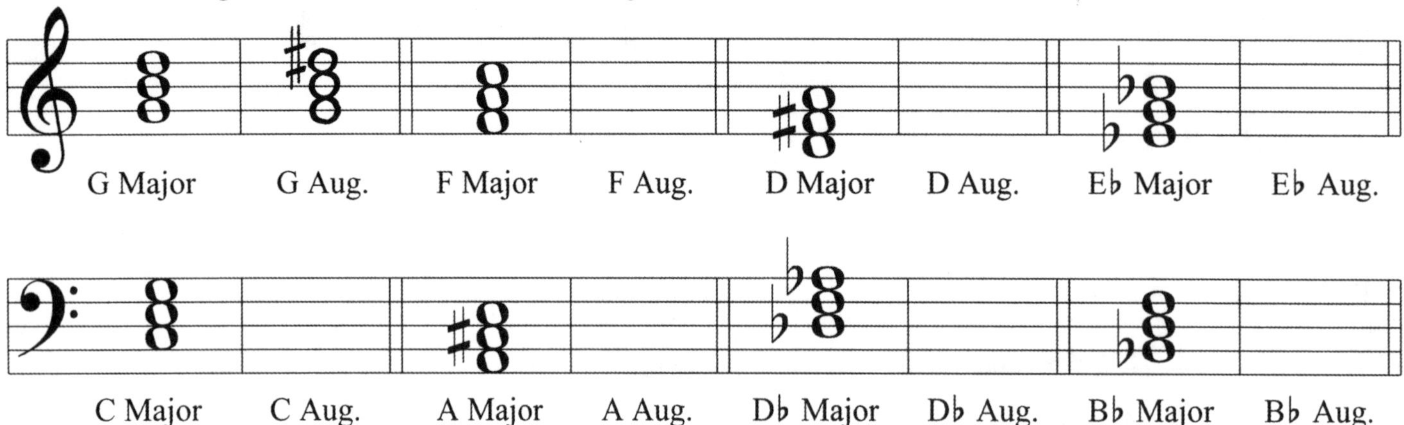

6. Name these triads. Write **M** for Major and **Aug.** for Augmented.

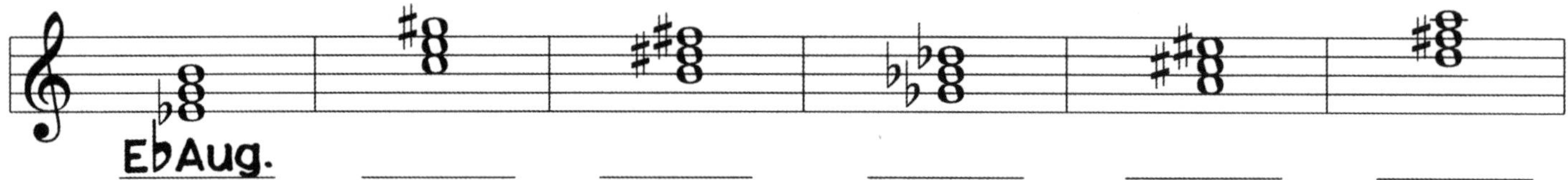

7. This piece uses Major and Augmented triads. Play this piece and name each triad.

Diminished Triads

A **diminished** triad is formed by lowering the 5th of a minor triad one half step.

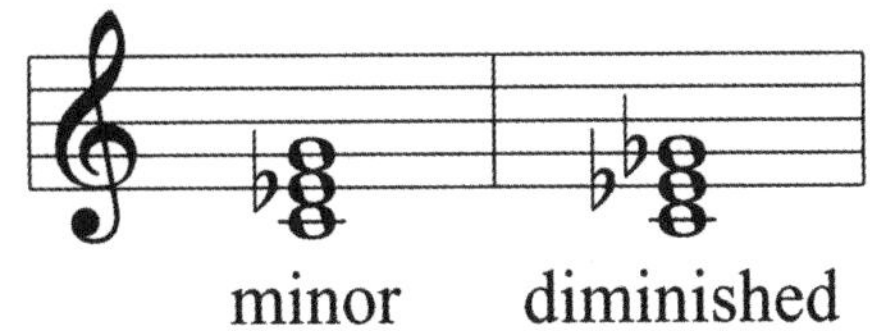

8. Draw a diminished triad after each minor triad.

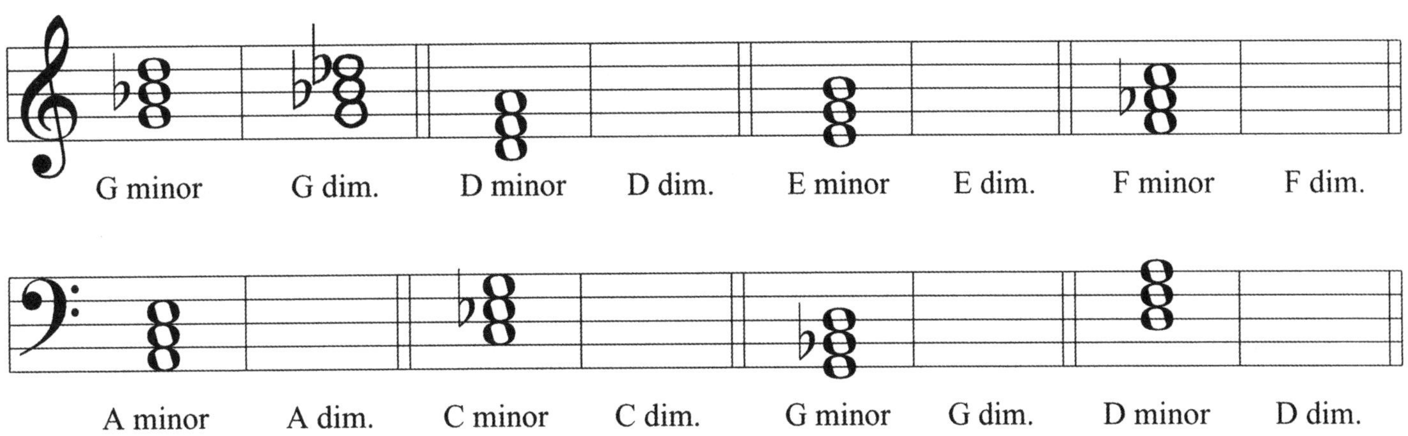

9. Name these triads. Write **m** for minor and **dim.** for diminished.

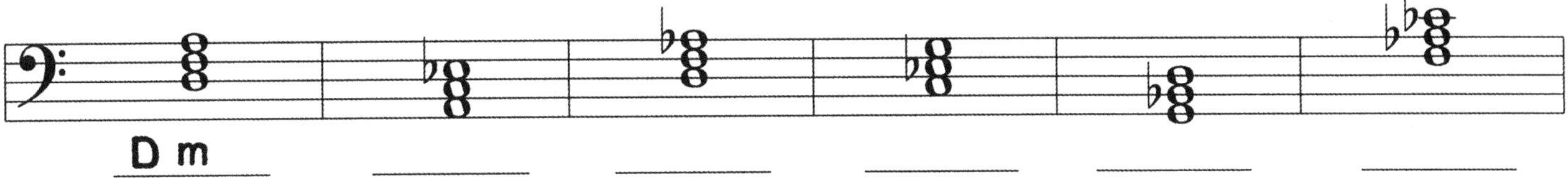

10. This piece uses minor, diminished, Major, and Augmented triads.
Play this piece and name each triad.

Unit 7
Triads and Inversions

The notes of a root position triad may be rearranged to form **inversions.**

- A triad is in **root position** when the root of the triad is the lowest note.
- A triad is in **1st inversion** when the 3rd of the triad is the lowest note.
- A triad is in **2nd inversion** when the 5th of the triad is the lowest note.

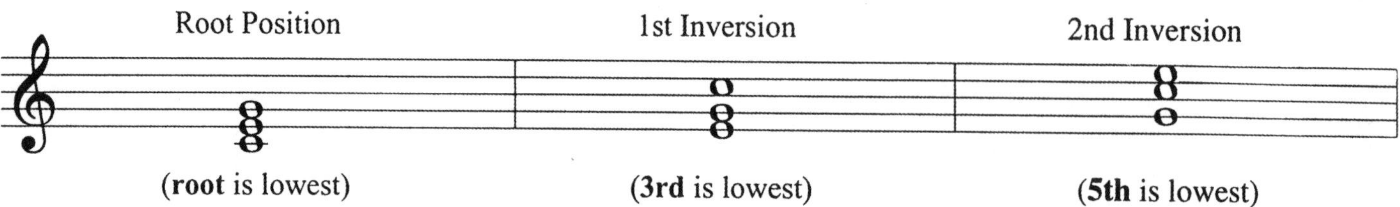

1. Draw these triads in root position, 1st inversion, and 2nd inversion.

Root Position | 1st inversion | 2nd inversion | Root Position | 1st inversion | 2nd inversion

D Major | F minor

B♭ Major | A minor

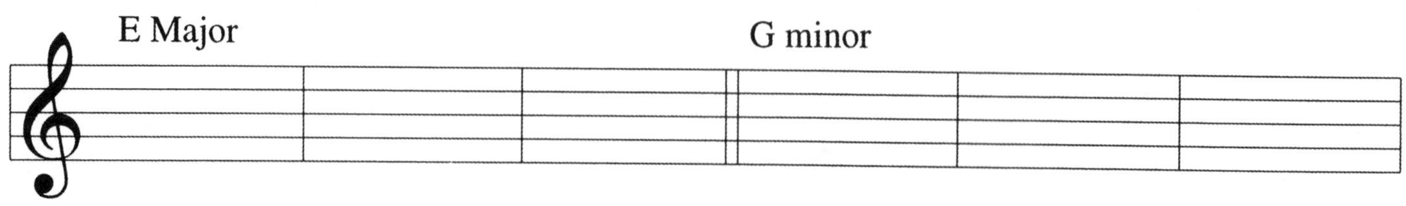

G Major | C minor

Identifying 1st and 2nd Inversion Triads

1st and 2nd inversion triads may be identified by their intervals.
The intervals are measured from the lowest note.

- **1st inversion** triads have the intervals of a **6th** and a **3rd.**

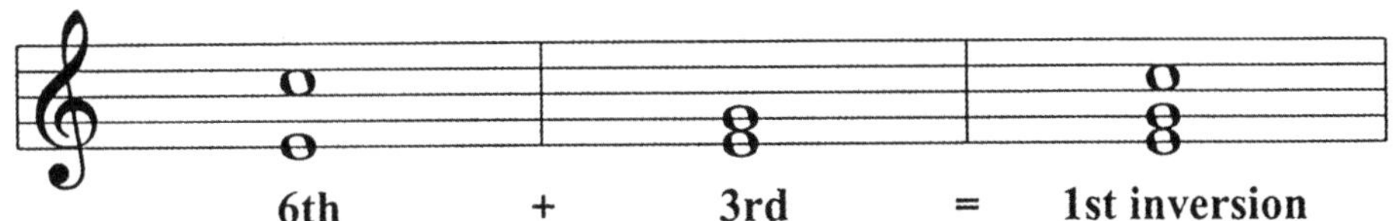

- **2nd inversion** triads have the intervals of a **6th** and a **4th.**

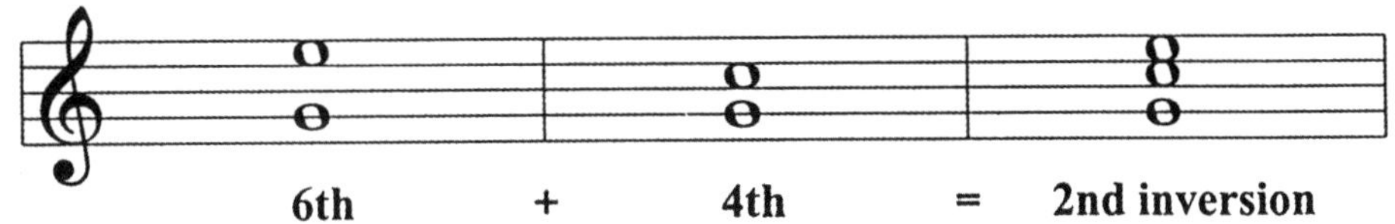

2. Name the root in these **1st inversion** triads.

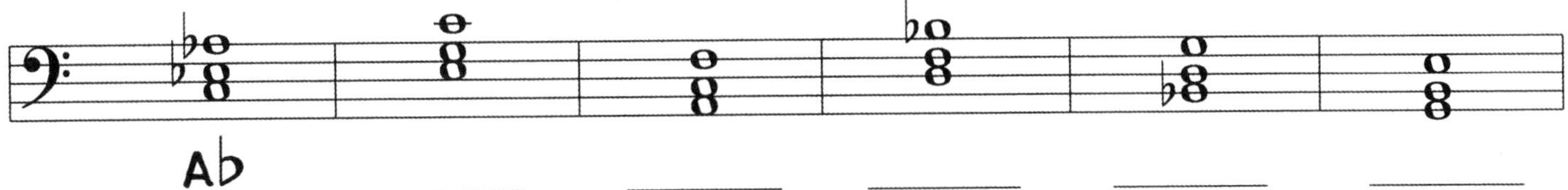

3. Name the root in these **2nd inversion** triads.

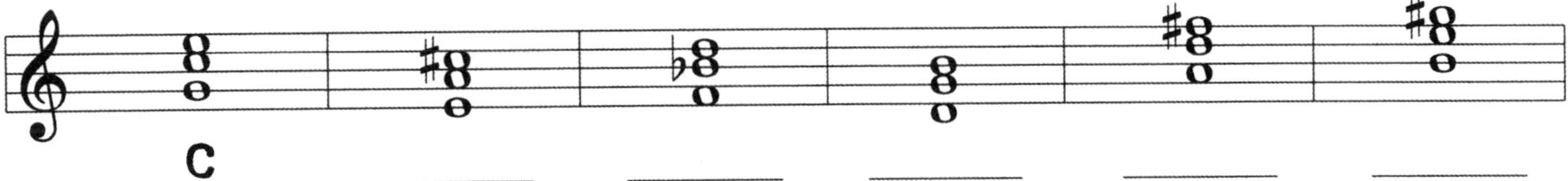

4. Draw these triads.

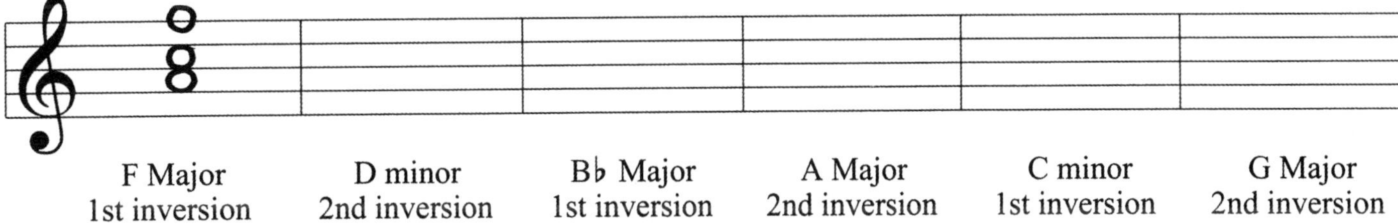

5. Name the root and the inversion of each triad.

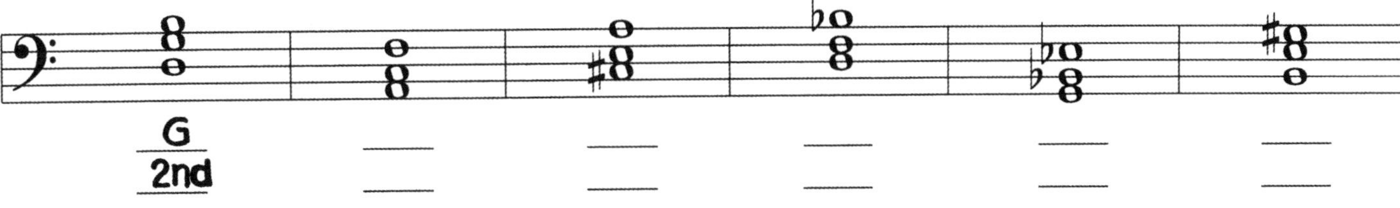

Unit 8

Primary Triads

Triads built on the first, fourth, and fifth notes of a scale are called **primary triads.**
Primary triads are labeled with Roman numerals: **I, IV, V.**
Each triad has a name: **I = tonic, IV = subdominant, V = dominant.**

Primary Triads in Major Keys

In Major keys, the primary triads are **Major** triads.

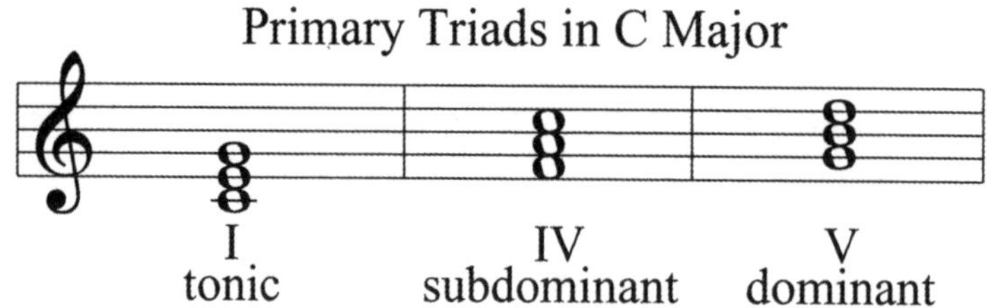

1. Name the Major key signature, then draw the primary triads for that key.

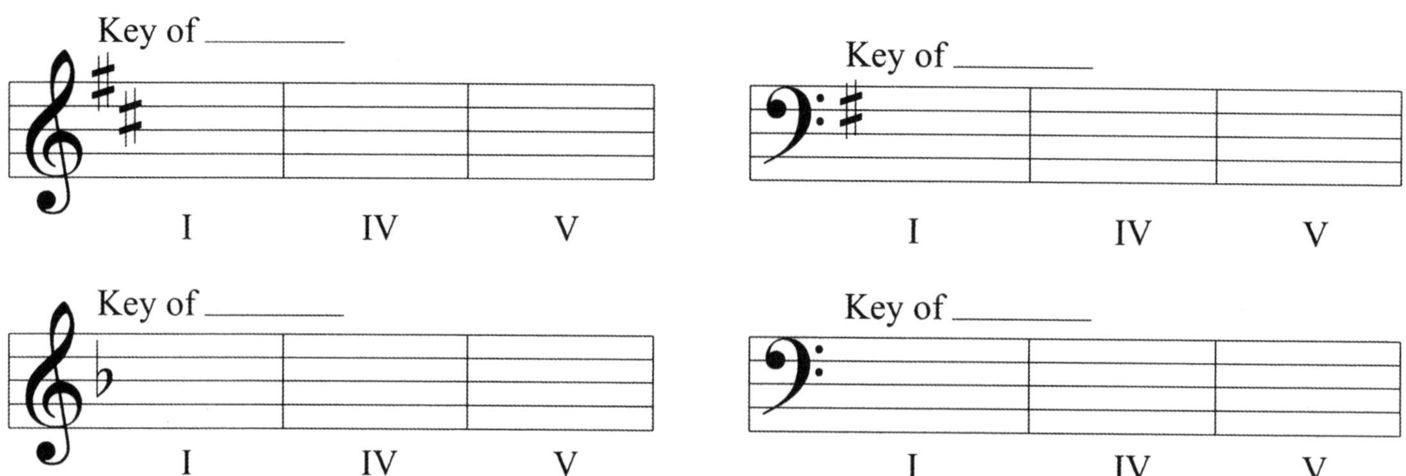

2. Add the correct sharps or flats to form primary triads in these Major Keys.

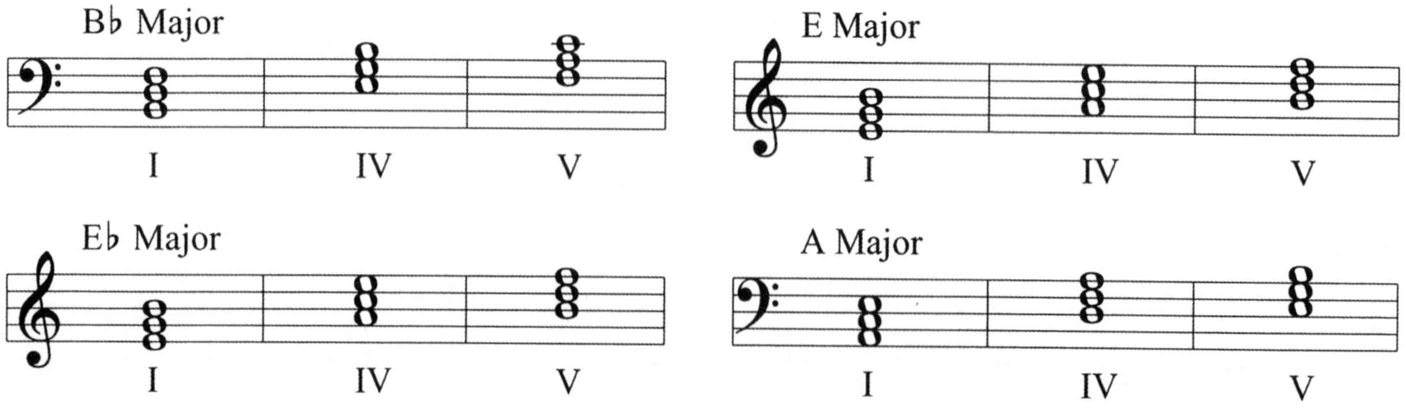

Primary Triads in Minor Keys

In minor keys, the tonic and subdominant triads are **minor** triads.
The dominant triad is **Major.***

Lower case Roman numerals are used to label minor triads.

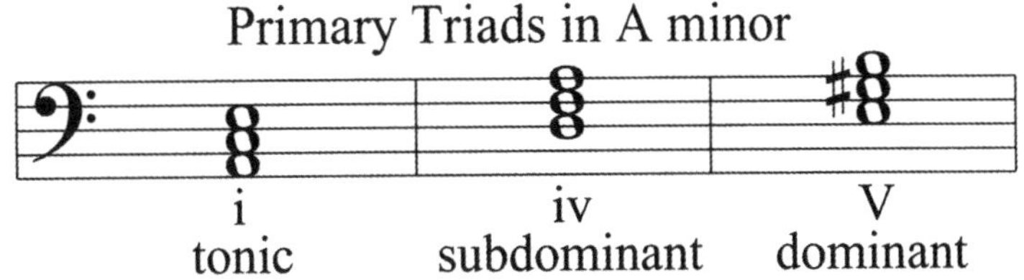

3. Name the minor key signature, then draw the primary triads for that key.

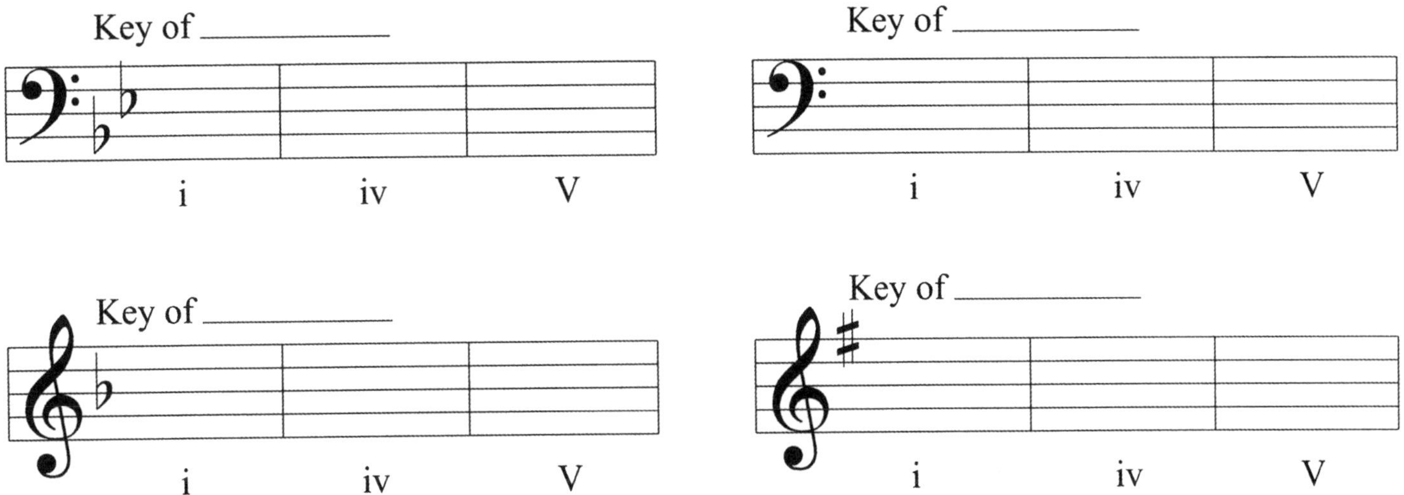

4. Add the correct sharps or flats to form primary triads in these minor keys.

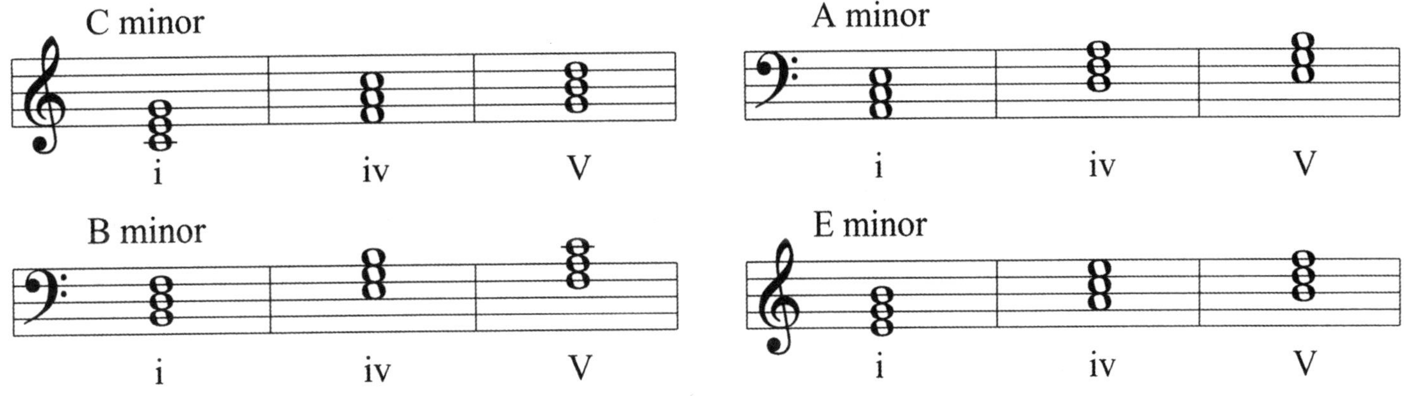

* The harmonic minor scale is used when forming the primary triads in a minor key.
The raised 7th note of the harmonic minor scale creates a dominant triad that is Major.

Unit 9

Cadences

A **cadence** is the combination of chords used at the end of a phase, section, or piece of music. Three types of cadences use primary triads: **V - I, IV - I, I - V.**
Each cadence has a name: V - I = **authentic,** IV - I = **plagal,** I - V = **half*.**

Root Position Cadences

Key of C Major

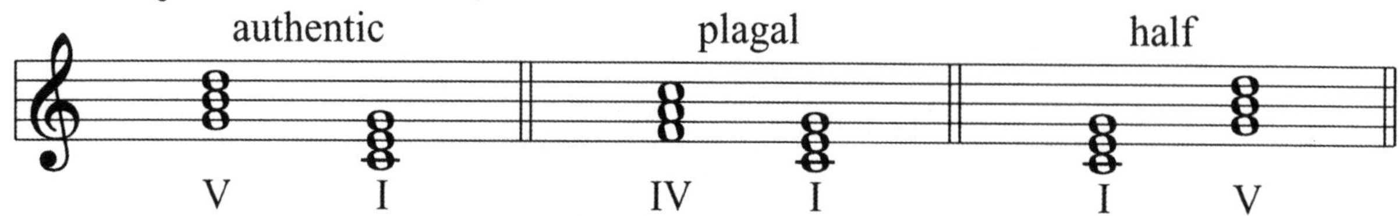

1. Draw these cadences with primary triads in root position. Label the triads with Roman numerals.

authentic plagal half

D Major

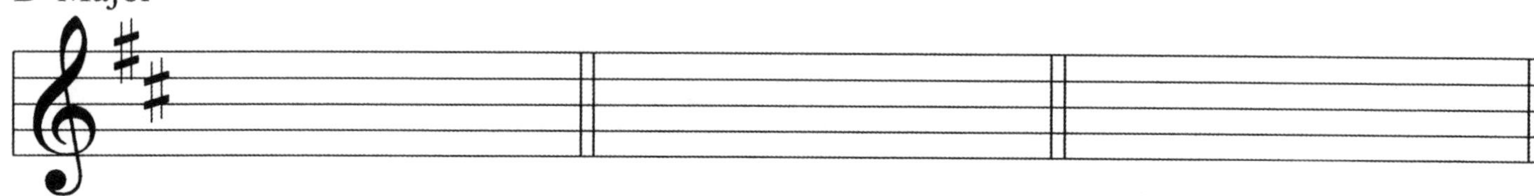

G Major

F Major

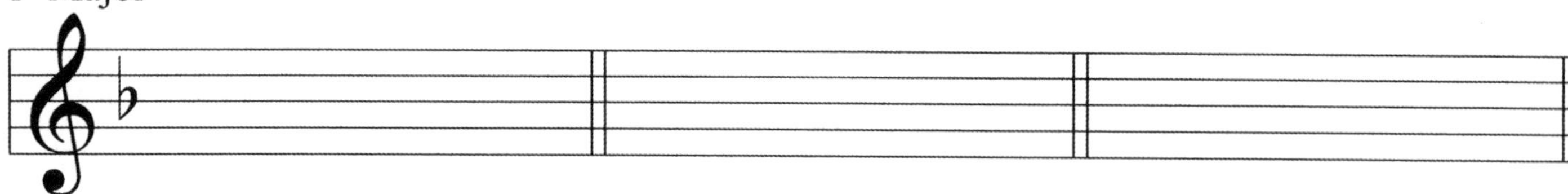

A minor (harmonic)

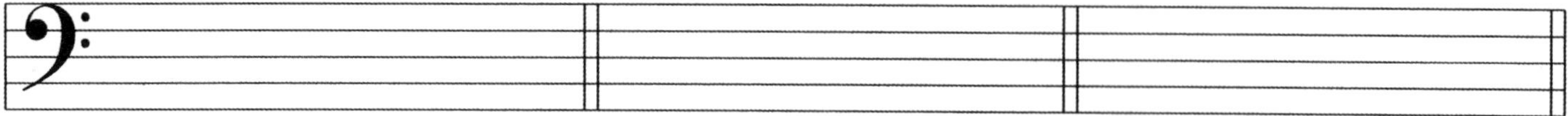

D minor (harmonic)

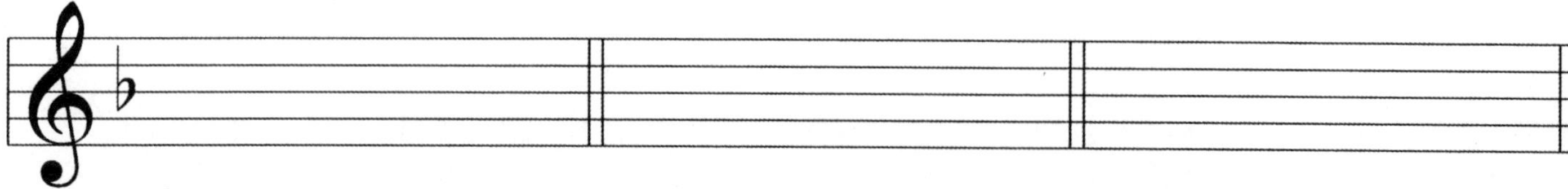

* A **half cadence** is any cadence which ends on the dominant.
Another example of half cadence is IV-V.

Common Note Cadences

Cadences are often written with the subdominant (IV) and dominant (V) triads inverted, creating a **common note** with the tonic (I) triad.

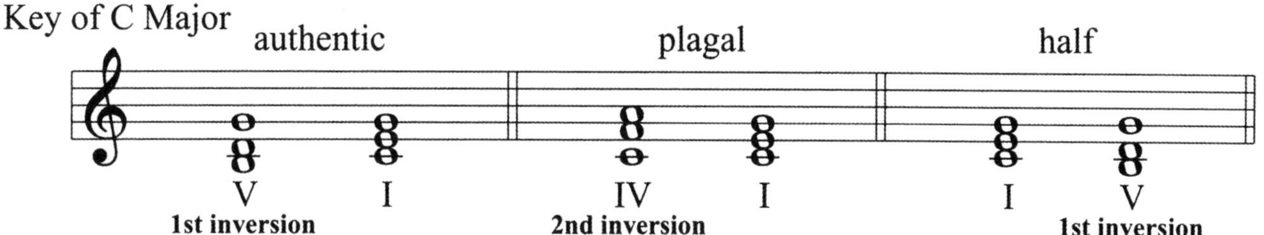

2. Draw these common note cadences with the **tonic** triad (I) in **root position, subdominant** triad (IV) in **2nd inversion,** and **dominant** triad (V) in **1st inversion.**
   Label the triads with Roman numerals.

authentic plagal half

D Major

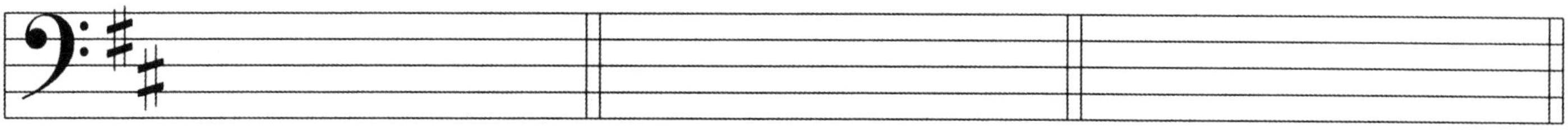

G Major

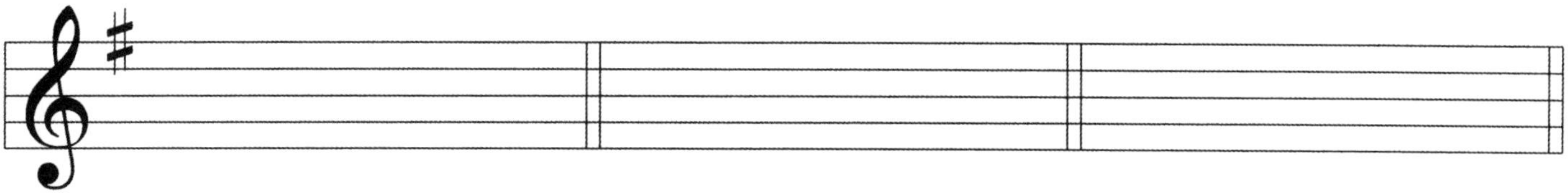

F Major

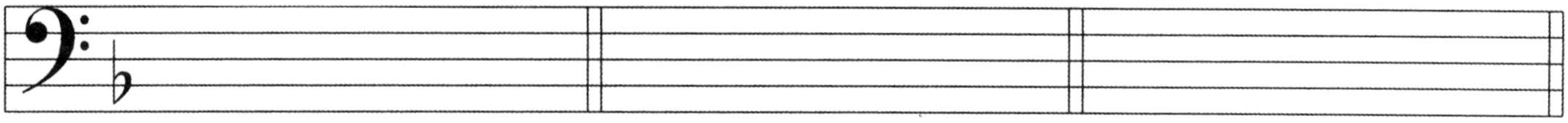

A minor (harmonic)

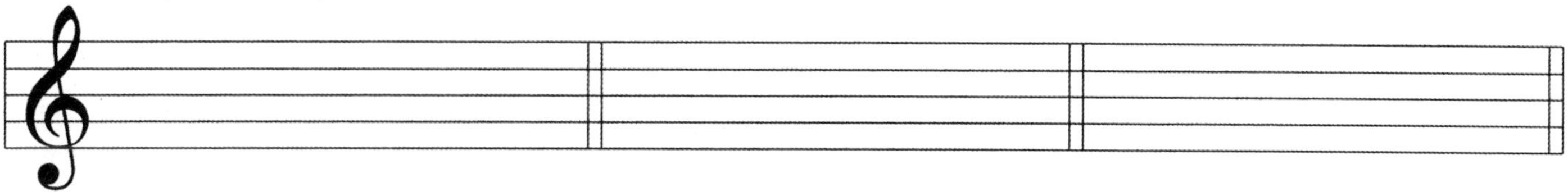

D minor (harmonic)

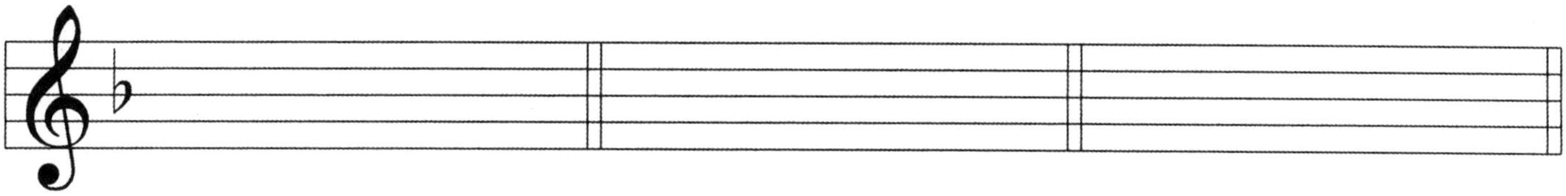

Unit 10

Dominant Seventh Chords

Root Position

A seventh chord has four notes: root, third, fifth, and seventh.

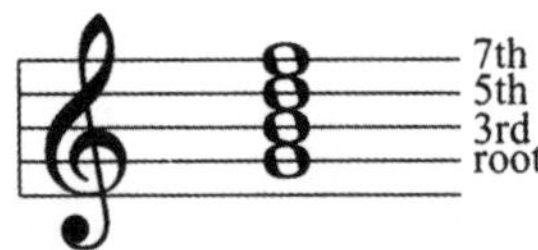

The dominant seventh (V7) chord in root position is built on the 5th note of the scale.

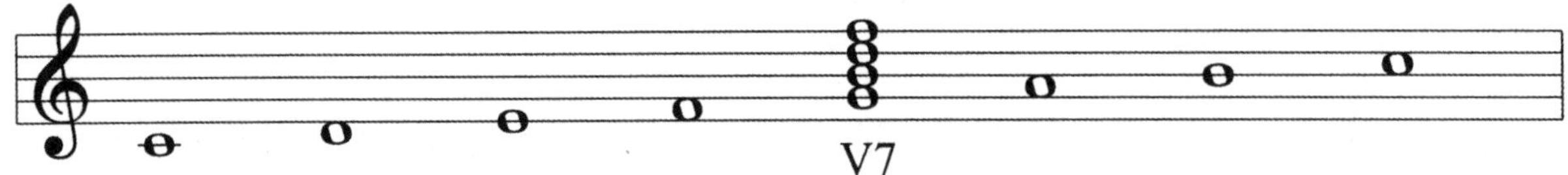

1. Draw a dominant seventh (V7) chord on the 5th note of each scale.

G Major

V7

D Major

V7

F Major

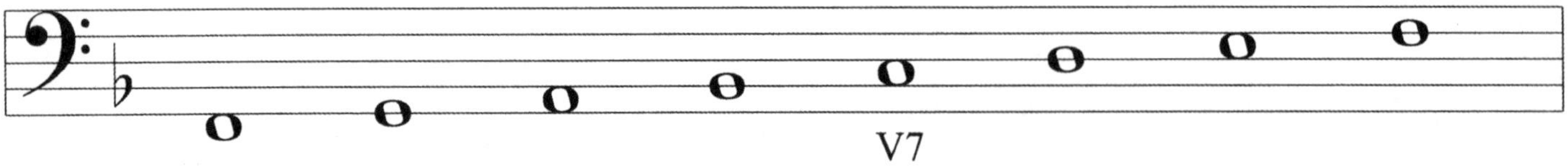

V7

B♭ Major

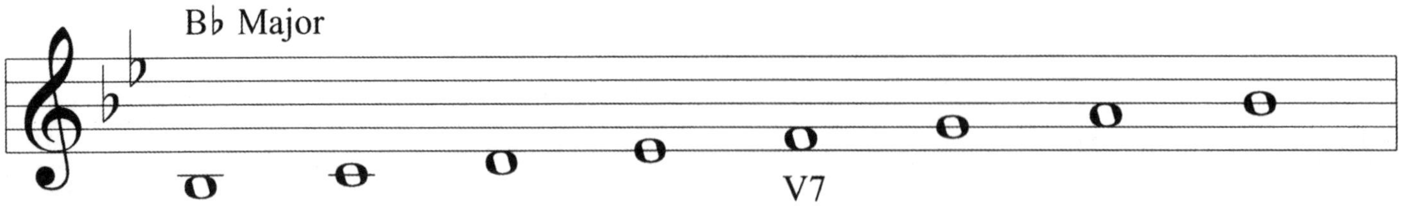

V7

A minor (harmonic)

V7

2. Circle and label root position dominant seventh (V7) chords in each example. The chords may be blocked or broken. The 3rd or 5th of the chord may appear in the melody.

1st Inversion Dominant Seventh Chords

The dominant seventh (V7) chord has three **inversions.**

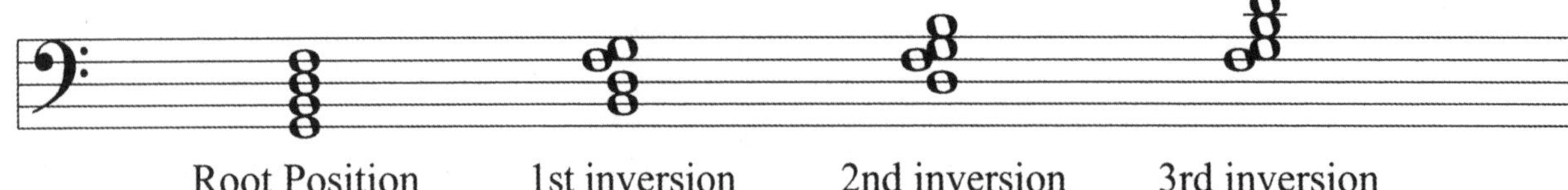

The **1st inversion** dominant seventh (V7) chord often appears in music with the fifth omitted.

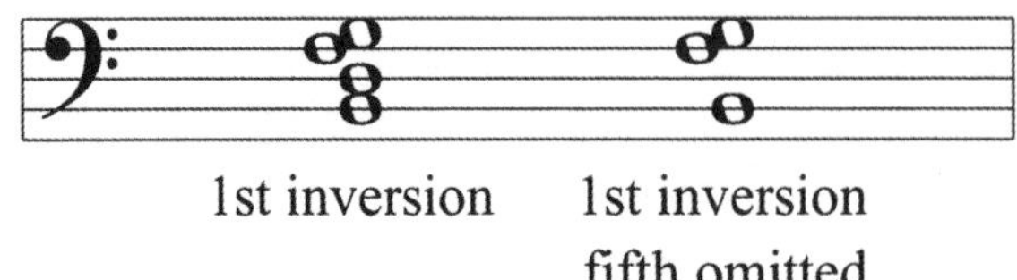

3. Draw these 1st inversion dominant seventh (V7) chords with the 5th omitted.

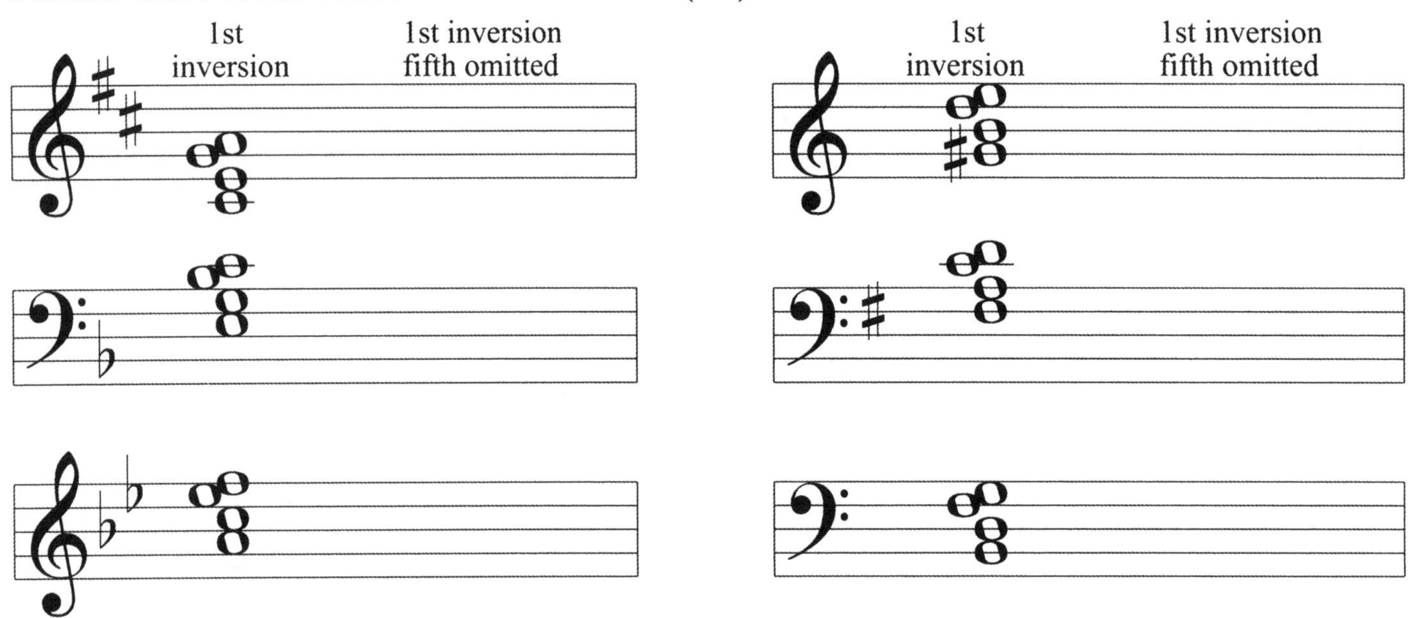

Authentic Cadence: V7 - I

4. Play these authentic cadences which use the 1st inversion dominant seventh (V7) chord. Label the chords with Roman numerals.

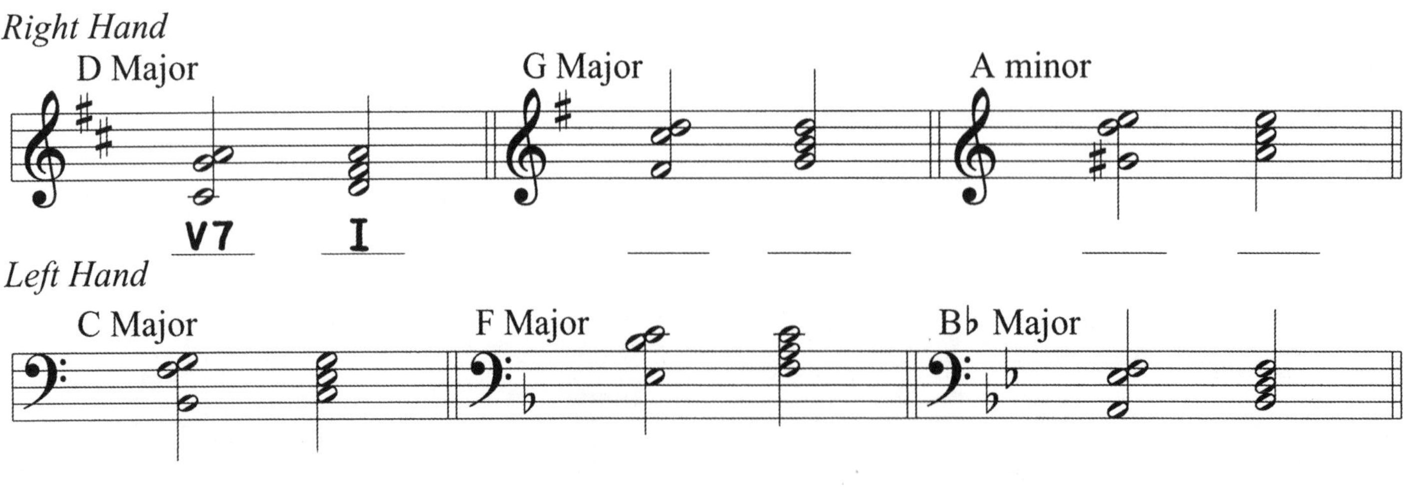

Primary Chord Progression: I IV V7

A **chord progression** is a series of chords. A **primary chord progression** uses only primary chords.

Primary chord progressions are often written with the subdominant (IV) chord in **2nd inversion** and the dominant seventh (V7) chord in **1st inversion** with the 5th omitted.

Primary Chord Progression in C Major

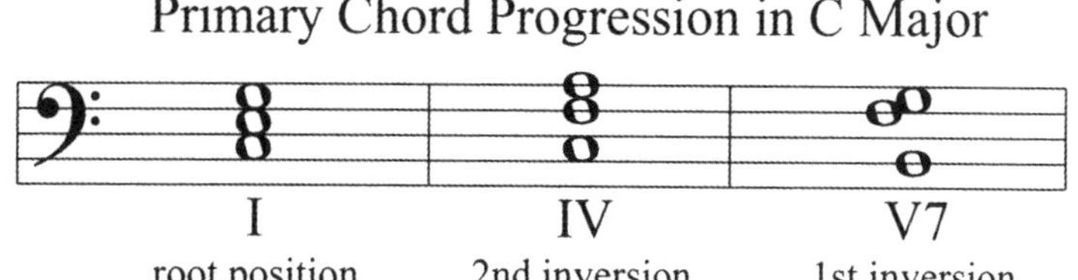

I	IV	V7
root position	2nd inversion	1st inversion

5. Draw these primary chord progressions.

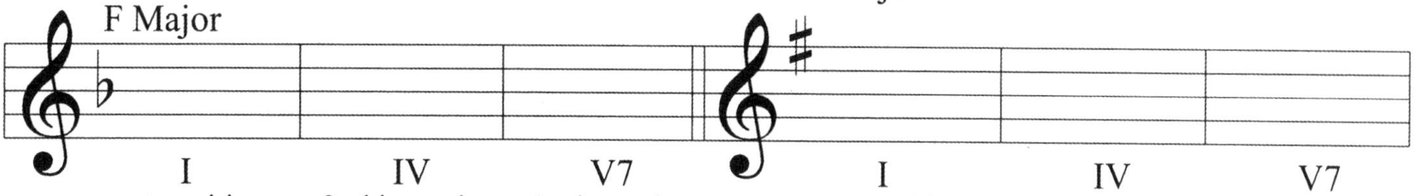

F Major

I	IV	V7
root position	2nd inversion	1st inversion

G Major

I	IV	V7
root position	2nd inversion	1st inversion

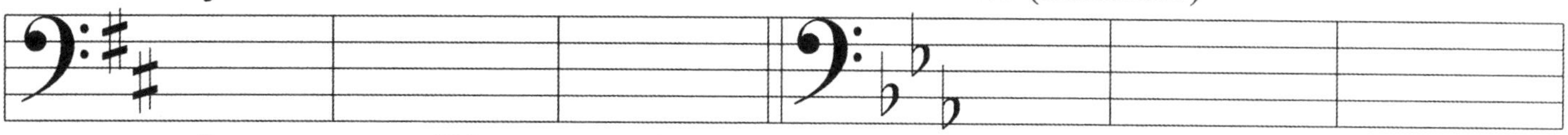

D Major

I	IV	V7
root position	2nd inversion	1st inversion

C minor (harmonic)

I	IV	V7
root position	2nd inversion	1st inversion

C Major

I	IV	V7
root position	2nd inversion	1st inversion

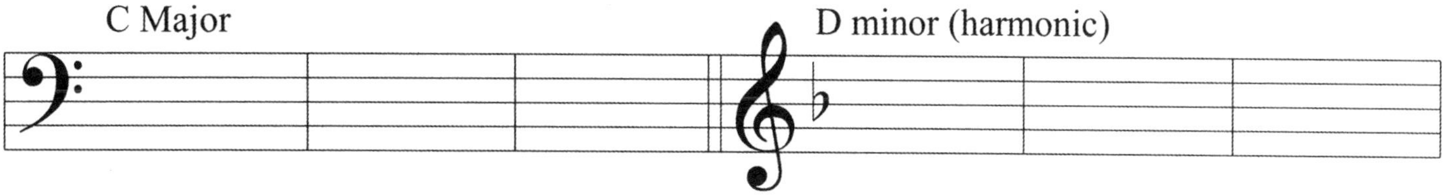

D minor (harmonic)

I	IV	V7
root position	2nd inversion	1st inversion

6. Play these primary chord progressions. Name each chord.

Key of __________

Key of __________

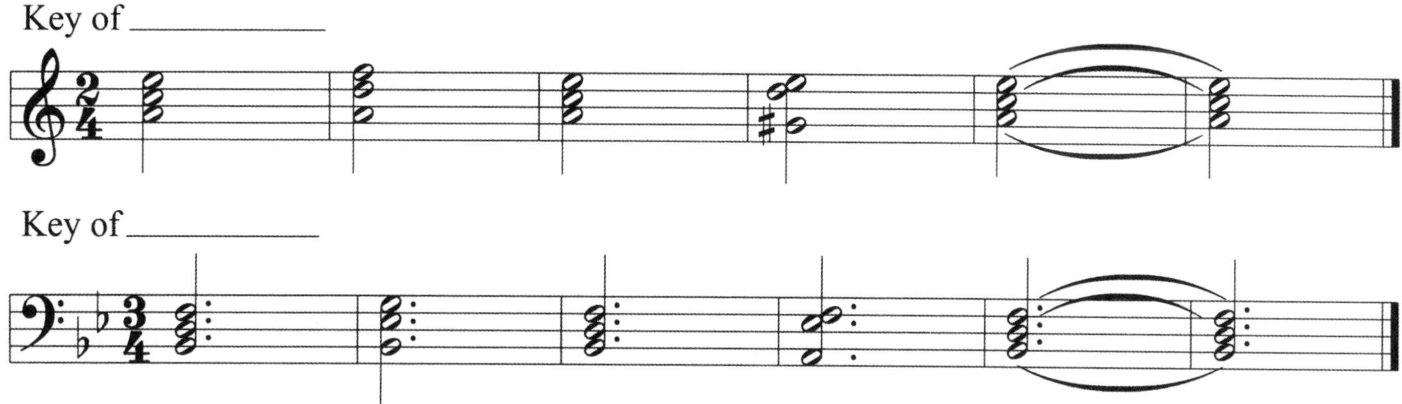

7. Write Roman numerals for the underlined chords in the music below.

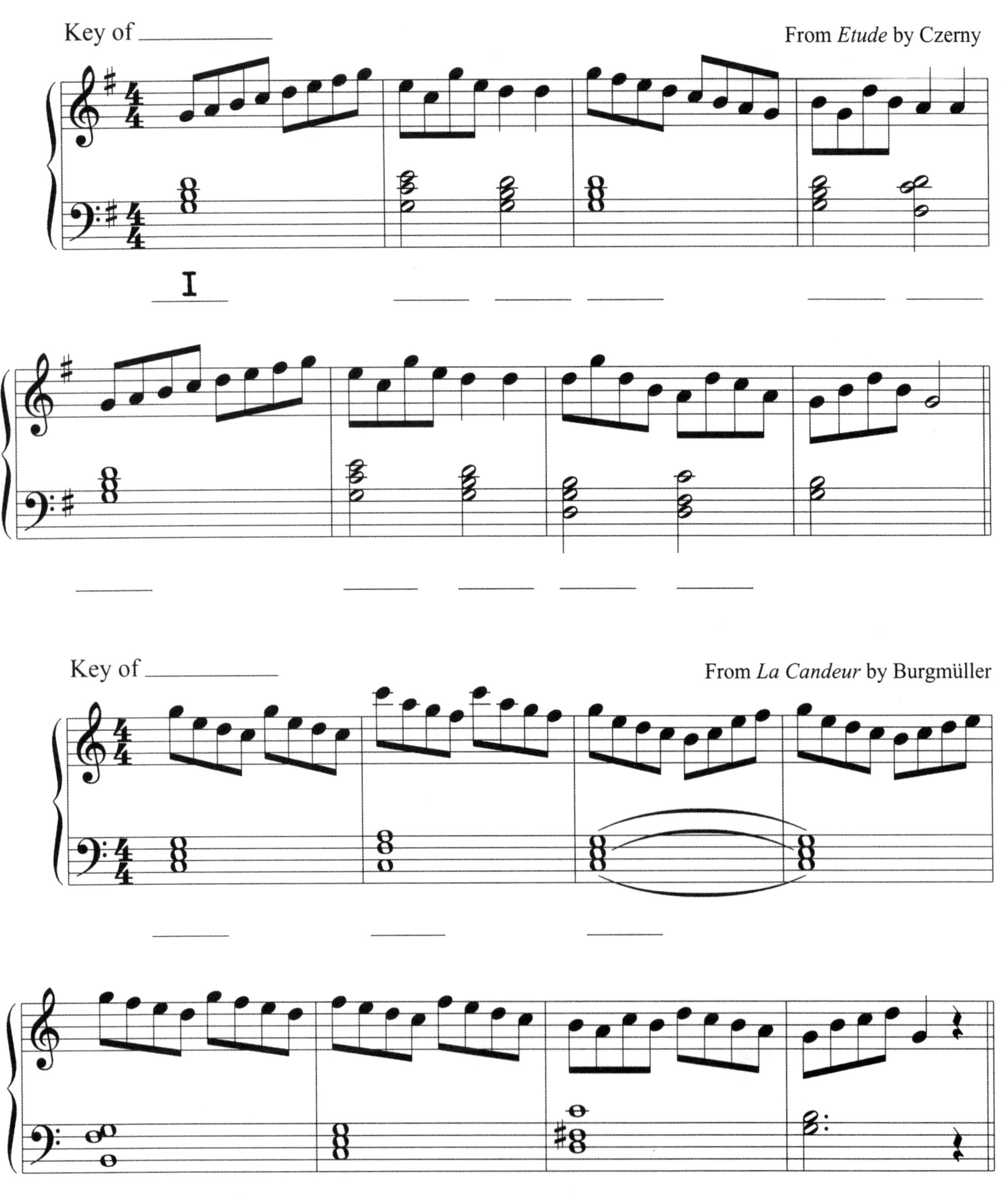

8. Harmonize this melody with primary chords. Use one chord in each measure *

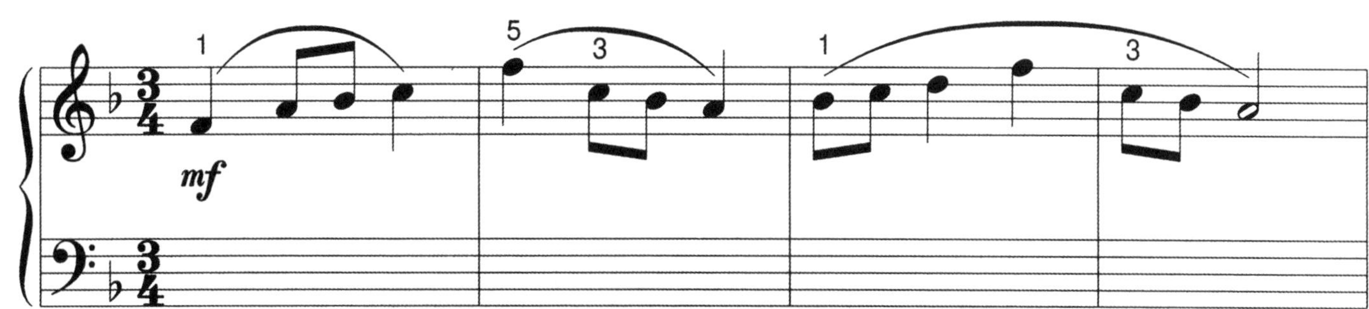

9. Transpose to D Major.

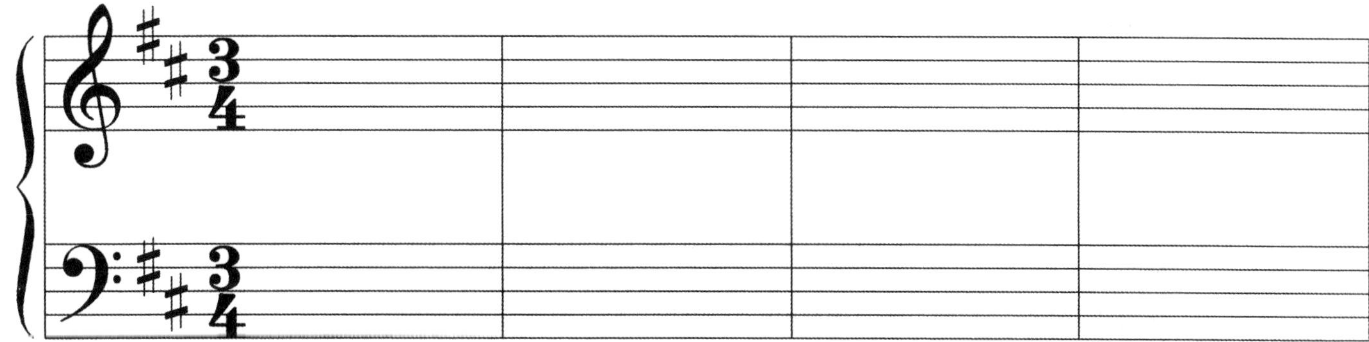

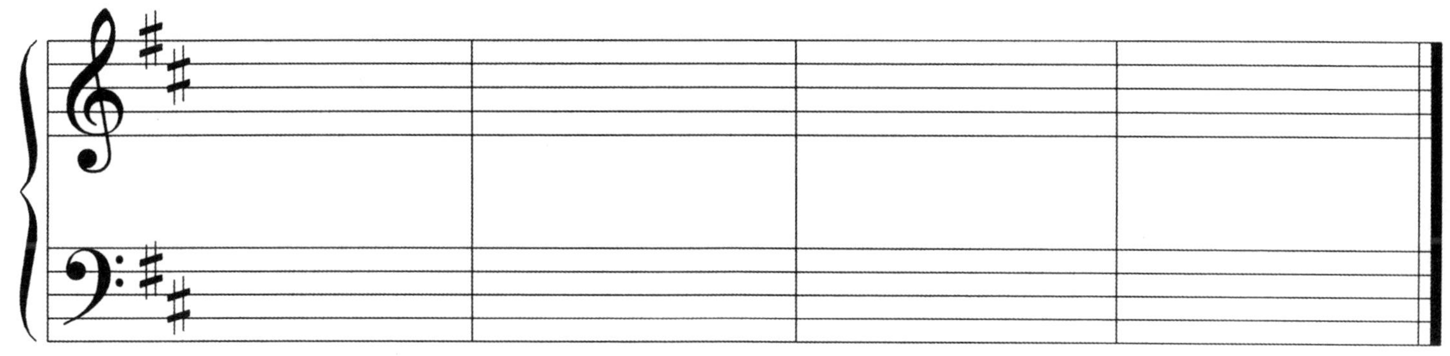

** Chords may be written blocked or broken.*

Unit 11

Signs and Terms

Dynamics

Dynamic signs tell how loud or soft to play.

TERM	SIGN	MEANING
pianississimo	***ppp***	very, very soft
pianissimo	***pp***	very soft
piano	***p***	soft
mezzo piano	***mp***	medium soft
mezzo forte	***mf***	medium loud
forte	***f***	loud
fortissimo	***ff***	very loud
fortississimo	***fff***	very, very loud
crescendo (cresc.)	(crescendo hairpin)	gradually louder
diminuendo (dim.)	(diminuendo hairpin)	gradually softer

Articulation

Articulation signs tell how to touch and release the keys.

TERM	SIGN	MEANING
accent	(notes with accent marks)	strong emphasis
legato	(slur)	smooth, connected
sforzando	***sf*** or ***sfz***	sudden, strong accent
staccato	(notes with staccato dots)	short, detached
tenuto	(notes with tenuto lines)	hold full value; slight emphasis

Tempo

Tempo marks tell how fast or slow to play.

TERM	MEANING
adagio	slow
allegro	fast (also means cheerful, happy)
allegretto	somewhat fast (slower than allegro)
andante	walking tempo (flowing)
andantino	slightly faster than andante
con brio	with spirit
con moto	with motion
lento	slow
moderato	moderately
vivace	lively, quick
vivo	lively

Changing Tempo

accelerando (accel.)	gradually faster
a tempo	return to the original tempo
ritardando (rit.)	gradually slower

Character or Style

These words help establish feeling, mood, or performance style.

TERM	MEANING
cantabile	in a singing manner
dolce	gently, sweetly
espressivo	expressively
giocoso	humorous
molto	much, very
poco	little
scherzando	playful
spiritoso	spirited

More Signs and Terms

D. C. al Fine (da capo al fine): Play from the beginning to the *fine* (end).

Fermata 𝄐 **:** Hold a note longer than its time value.

Grace Note **:** A grace note is printed in small type. It is not counted in the rhythm; it is played quickly, almost together with the next note.

Motive (motif) **:** a short musical idea.

Octave Sign *8va- - - - -*
When the octave sign is placed **over** notes, play one octave (eight notes) **higher** than written. When the octave sign is placed **under** notes, play them one octave **lower** than written.

Pedal Sign **:**The pedal sign shows when to press and lift the damper (right) pedal.

Repeat Signs

1. Repeat from the beginning.

2. Repeat between the pairs of dots and double bar lines.

3. 1. 2. Play the **first ending** and repeat from the beginning; then skip the first ending and play the **second ending.**

Repetition: Exact repeat of a note or rhythm pattern.

Sequence: Repetition of a melodic pattern at a higher or lower pitch; usually a 2nd or 3rd above or below.

Slur **:** A curved line over or under two or more notes that are to be played legato.

Tie **:** A curved line that connects notes on the same line or space. Play only the first note and hold it for the value of both notes.

tre corde : Release the soft (left) pedal.

una corda : Depress the soft (left) pedal.

Signs and Terms Review

1. Write the meaning of each term.

poco ______________________ spiritoso______________________

molto ______________________ dolce ______________________

adagio ______________________ accelerando______________________

a tempo______________________ allegretto ______________________

2. Draw a line to match the signs and terms.

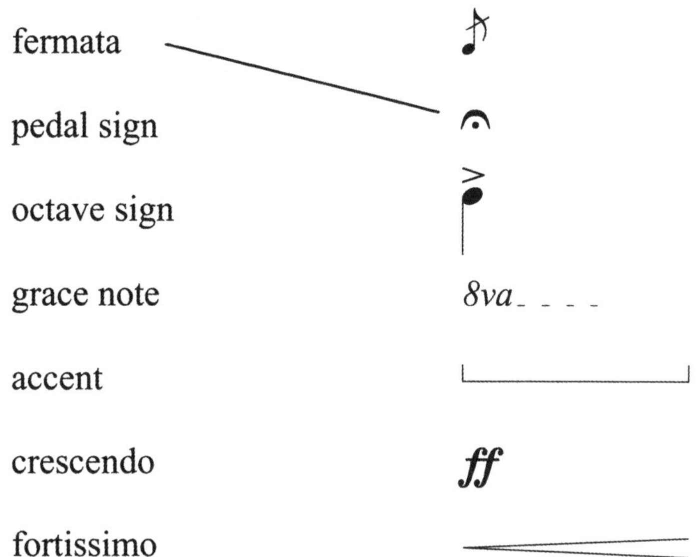

3. Write the term for each meaning.

sudden, strong accent ______________________ fast ______________________

playful ______________________ in a singing manner ______________________

smooth, connected ______________________ moderately______________________

with motion______________________ very loud ______________________

Unit 12

Structure, Style and Form in Music

Melodic Phrase Structure

Question and Answer Phrases

A melody often has two parts: a **question** phrase and an **answer** phrase.
The question phrase will end on a note other than the tonic.
The answer phrase will end on the tonic.

The music below is an example of question and answer phrases in **four measures:** a two measure question phrase, and a two measure answer phrase.

From *Polonaise* by Bach

Question Phrase **Answer Phrase**

The music below is an example of question and answer phrases in **eight measures:** a four measure question phrase, and a four measure answer phrase.

From *German Dance* by Haydn

Question Phrase

Answer Phrase

1. Look at pieces you are learning to play and identify question and answer phrases.

Repetition

Repetition occurs when a melodic or rhythmic pattern is repeated.

The music below is an example of a two measure repetition. Notice that the rhythm of the left hand notes is changed slightly in the final measure: a small change may occur in a repetition.

From *Polonaise* by Bach

Sequence

A sequence occurs when a melodic pattern in repeated at a higher or lower pitch, usually a 2nd or 3rd above or below the original pattern.

In the musical example below, the sequence moves up by the interval of a 2nd. Notice that in the final sequence, the last notes are changed to lead smoothly into the cadence.

From *Minuet* by Handel

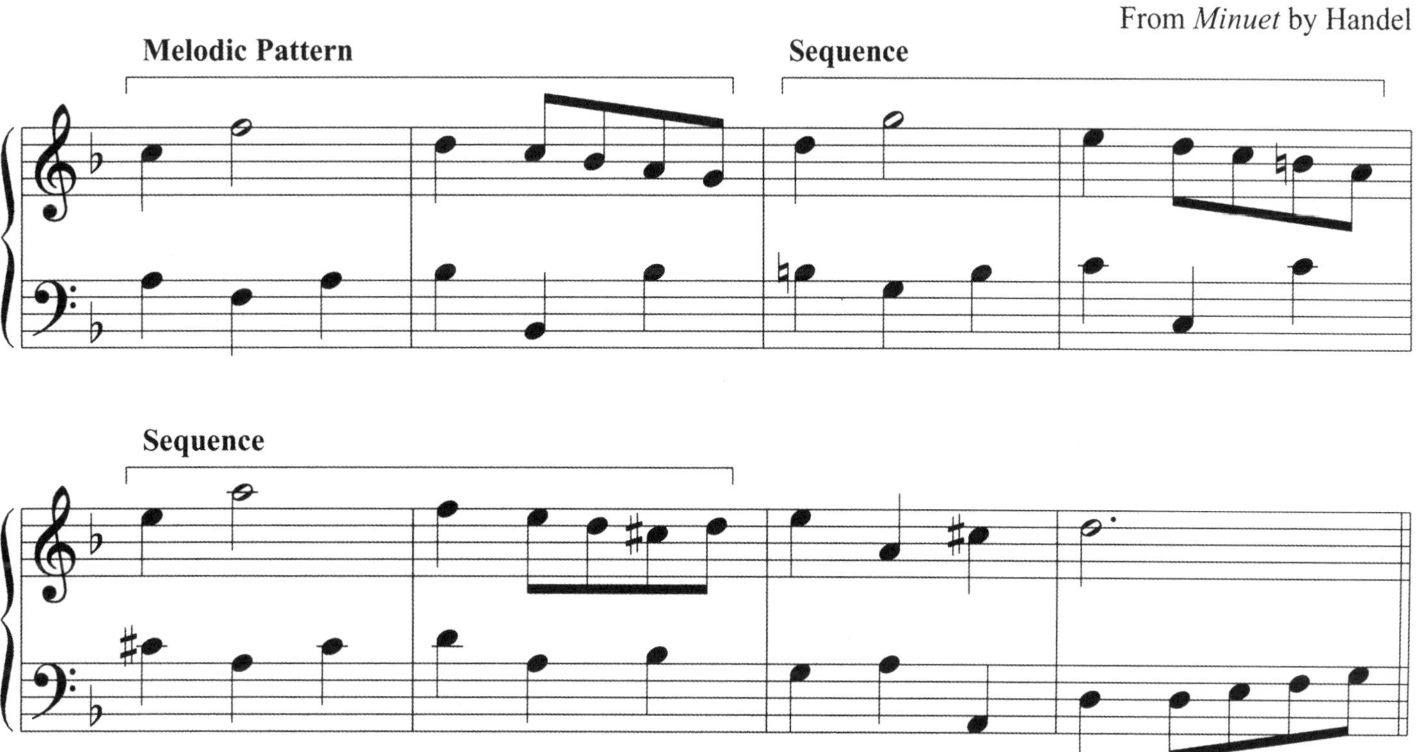

2. Look at pieces you are learning to play and identify repetition and sequence.

Musical Styles

Polyphonic Music

Baroque keyboard music (1600-1750) was usually written with each hand playing its own melody or "voice". This style of music writing is called **polyphonic.**

In the musical examples below, notice that each hand is playing single notes: each hand has its own melody.

From *Aria* by Bach

From *Le Petit Rien* by Couperin

Homophonic Music

Classical (1750-1825) and Romantic (1825-1900) piano music was usually written with the right hand playing a melody and the left hand playing an accompaniment. This style of music writing is called **homophonic.**

In the musical examples below, notice that the accompaniment may be blocked or broken chords.

From *Arabesque* by Burgmüller

Blocked chord accompaniment

From *Waltz in A* by Schubert

Broken chord or "Waltz bass" accompaniment

From *Sonatina, Op. 36, No. 1,* by Clementi

Broken chord accompaniment

3. Look at pieces you are learning to play and identify them as polyphonic or homophonic.

Musical Forms

Binary Form

Music in binary form has two sections: section **A** and section **B**. Each section is usually repeated. The **A** section often ends on the *dominant* note, and the **B** section ends on the *tonic*.

Ternary Form

Music written in **ternary form** has three sections: section **A,** section **B,** and a repeat of section **A**. The two sections are often contrasting in character or style.

Scherzo from Sonata in F

by Haydn

4. Look at pieces you are learning to play and identify them as binary or ternary. Mark the sections **A** and **B.**

Sonatina

A sonatina is a short sonata. A sonatina may have one, two, or three movements. The movements are usually contrasting in tempo and character.

First Movement Form

First movements of sonatinas are frequently written in a form called *sonata allegro* or **first movement form:**

1. **Exposition** section
   A. first theme (tonic key)
   B. second theme (dominant key)
   C. closing theme (optional)
2. **Development** section
   Themes are presented in new keys. New themes may be added.
3. **Recapitulation** section
   A. first theme (tonic key)
   B. second theme (tonic key)
   C. closing theme (optional)

The following music is the first movement of a Sonatina by Clementi. The sections and themes have been marked to show the form of the piece. Identify sections and themes in a similar way whenever you learn to play sonatinas.

* A **motive** is a short melodic or rhythmic pattern that appears throughout a piece. When the motive appears in the music, it may begin on a different note, the rhythm may change slightly, or the motive may even appear upside down!

8 **Second Theme** (dominant key: G Major)

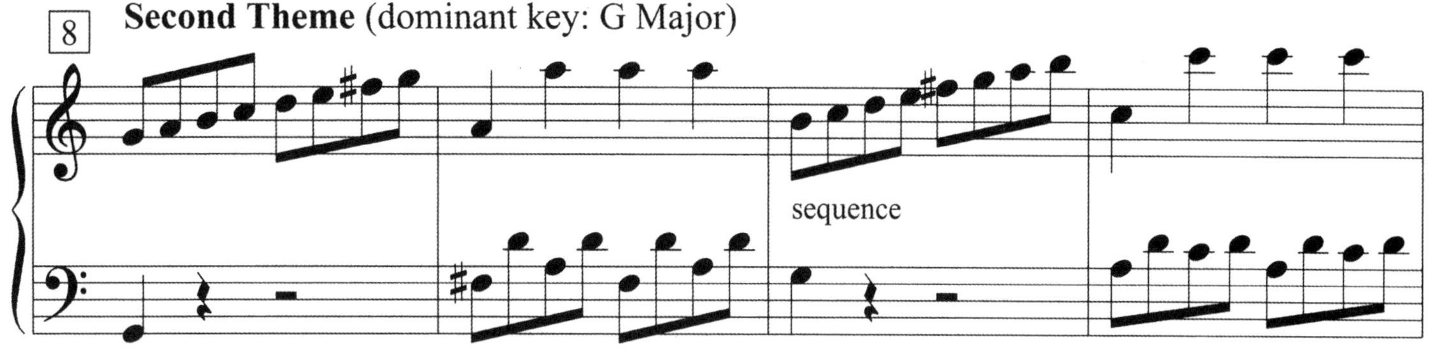

12 **Closing Theme**

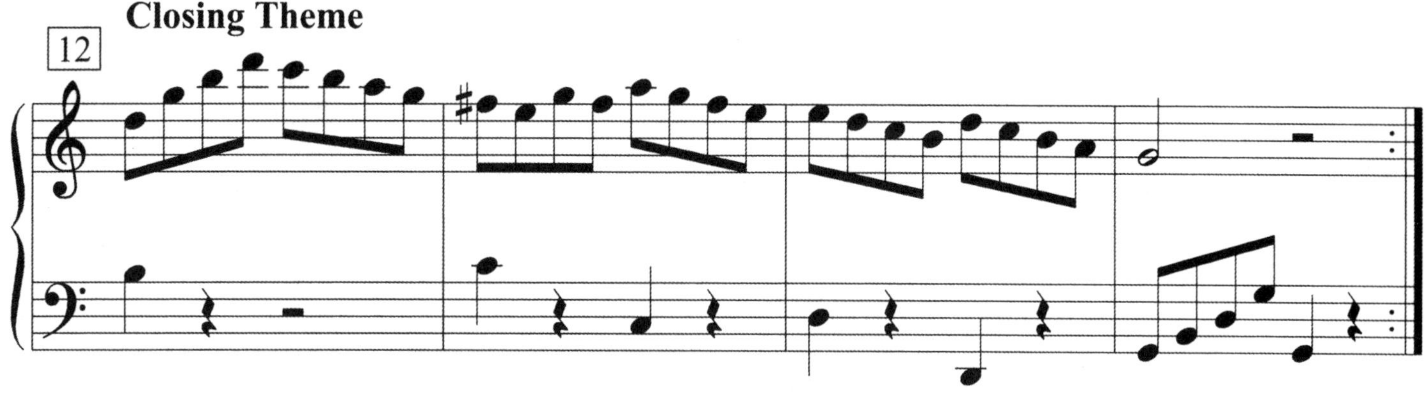

DEVELOPMENT

16 **First Theme** (New key: C minor)

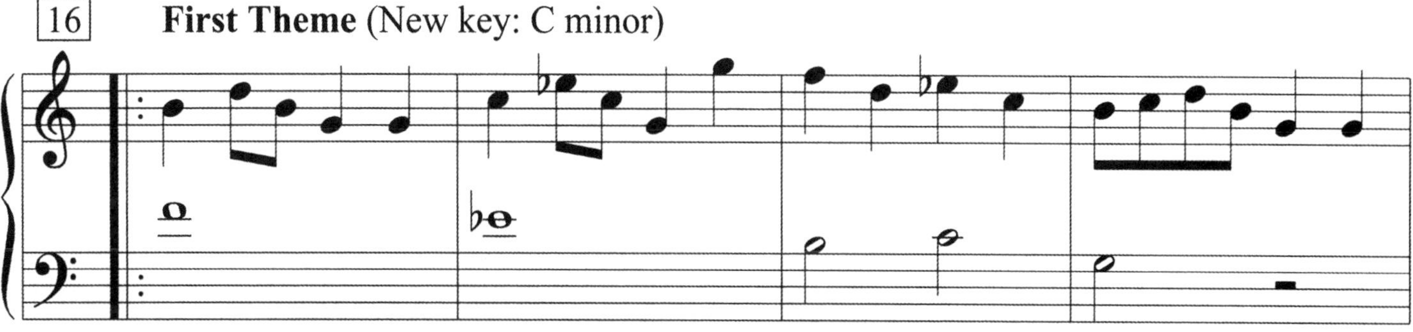

20

RECAPITULATION

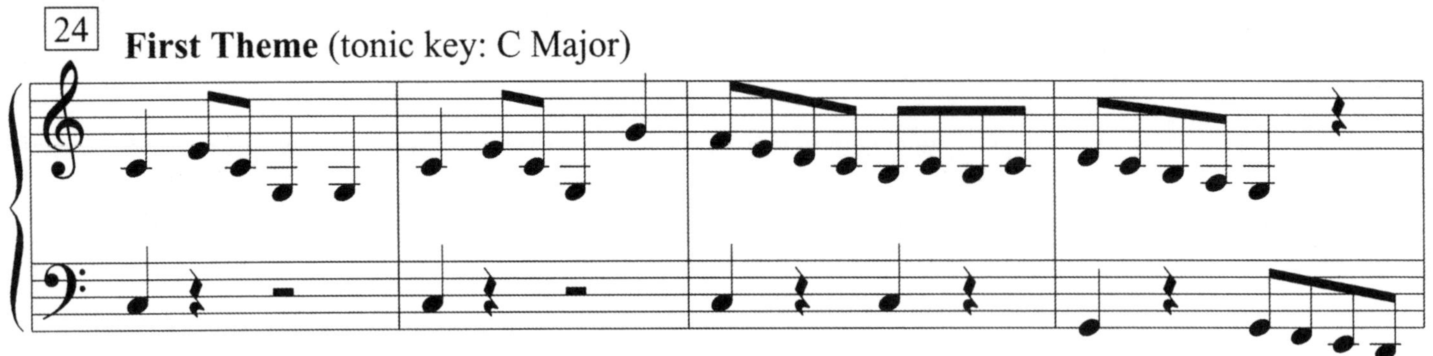

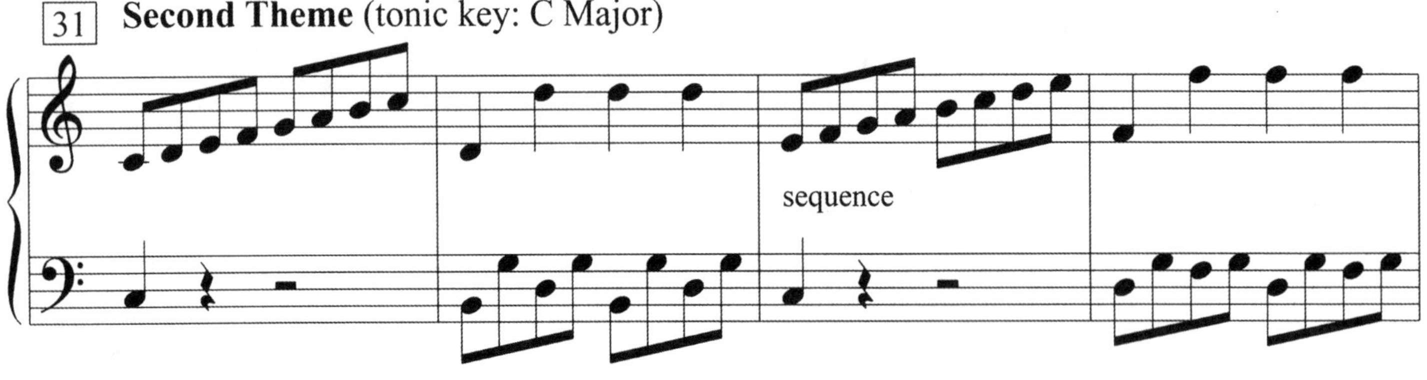

Answer these questions about the *Sonatina, Op. 36, No. 1*, first movement, by Clementi. (Measure numbers are found at the beginning of each line of music.)

1. In what measure does the exposition section begin? __________
2. In what measure does the first theme begin? __________
3. What is the key of the first theme? __________
4. What triad is formed by the notes in measure 1? __________
5. What note in measures 6 and 7 indicates a key change? __________
6. In what measure does the second theme begin? __________
7. What is the key of the second theme? __________
8. What Major scale is found in measure 8? __________
9. What triad is formed by the left hand notes in measure 9? __________
10. What is the inversion of the triad in measure 9? __________
11. In measure 11, the left hand notes form a dominant seventh chord. What note is missing: the third or the fifth? __________
12. The melodic pattern in measures 8 and 9 is repeated on different notes in measures 10 and 11. Is this an example of sequence or repetition? __________
13. In what measure does the development section begin? __________
14. Is the first or the second theme used in the development? __________
15. What is the key of the development? __________
16. What note in measure 17 makes this key minor? __________
17. The notes in measure 16 form a dominant seventh chord. Which hand plays the seventh of the chord? __________
18. What triad is formed by the notes in measure 17? __________
19. The left hand notes in measure 20 form a dominant seventh chord. What note is missing: the third or the fifth? __________
20. What triad is formed by the left hand notes measure 21? __________
21. What is the inversion of the triad in measure 21? __________
22. In what measure does the recapitulation begin? __________
23. In what key is the recapitulation? __________
24. In what measure does the second theme begin? __________
25. What major scale is found in measure 31? __________
26. What triad is formed by the left hand notes in measure 32? __________
27. What is the inversion of the triad in measure 32? __________
28. In measure 34, the left hand notes form a dominant seventh chord. What note is missing: the third or the fifth? __________
29. The melodic pattern in measures 31 and 32 is repeated on different notes in measures 33 and 34. Is this an example of sequence or repetition? __________
30. The motive in measure 1 appears ten times throughout this piece - sometimes slightly changed. Circle the motive each time it appears in the music.

Unit 13
The Four Periods of Music History

The history of music writing is generally divided into four basic periods. Each period has certain styles which make it unique. The four periods are:

1. The Baroque Period (1600 - 1750)

The term *Baroque* is used to described the style of music written from approximately 1600 to 1750. The term was originally used to describe a style of art and architecture of highly decorative and extravagant design in the 17th and 18th centuries. The elaborate detail of design during the Baroque period can also be seen in the very decorative furniture of the era. It was a time when people wore lavish clothes and ornamented themselves with ruffles, jewels, and powdered wigs!

Before the invention of the piano, keyboard music was written for the clavichord and the harpsichord. The clavichord produces a small, delicate sound and was used mainly in small rooms where it could be easily heard. The harpsichord has a bigger sound and was the favored instrument during the Baroque period.

Baroque keyboard music was frequently written in polyphonic style. Much of the music was written as dance pieces such as the *minuet, gavotte, gigue, polonaise, allemande,* and many others. Baroque keyboard pieces were often written in binary form.

Important Baroque composers:

Johann Sebastian Bach (Germany, 1685-1750)
Georg Philipp Telemann (Germany, 1681-1767)
Jean-Philippe Rameau (France, 1683-1764)
Domenico Scarlatti (b. Italy 1685 - d. Spain 1757)
George Frideric Handel (b. Germany 1685 - d. England 1759)

2. The Classical Period (1750 - 1825)

The classical period, dating from about 1750 to 1825, was a time of change from the decorative Baroque to a more simple style. The art and architecture of the period reflected these changes. Buildings were designed with simple, elegant lines defined by balanced form. People wore clothes tailored in a less elaborate manner than in the Baroque period and wore fewer wigs and lavish stylings.

Around the year 1700, an Italian named Bartolomeo Cristofori built a new instrument which he called a *gravicembalo col piano e forte* (a keyboard insrtument that can play loud and soft). Thus, Cristofori is credited with building the first piano. Other manufacturers throughout Europe were developing new instruments similar to Cristofori's during the 18th century. However, it was the design improvements made by Johann Stein in Vienna in the late 18th century that gave the piano its great popularity. It was these Viennese pianos that were used by composers such as Haydn, Mozart, and Beethoven.

Classical keyboard music was usually in homophonic style, and often written in ternary form. Although composers still wrote dance pieces, one of the most popular new forms was the *sonatina.* The *rondo* also became an important form during the Classical period.

Important Classical composers:

Joseph Haydn (Austria, 1732-1809)
Wolfgang Amadeus Mozart (Austria,1756 -1791)
Ludwig van Beethoven (Germany, 1770 -1827)
Muzio Clementi (b. Italy 1752-d. England 1832)

3. Romantic Period (1825 - 1900)

The French Revolution (1789-1794) stirred peoples' desire for freedom and individuality. Self expression became important for musicians, artists, and writers and they looked for new ways to express beauty and imagination. Even in dress, expressive beauty was portrayed. Women wore hoop skirts and decorative clothing with embroidery and lace. Men wore ruffled shirts, wide bow ties, and elegant clothes. Strong emphasis on emotion and imagination is found in the literature, art, and architecture of the period.

Pianos in the Romantic period developed into a larger instrument with a bigger and more resonant sound than the pianos of the Classical period. The piano gained great popularity during the 19th century, and piano lessons were considered an important part of a good education.

Piano music of the Romantic period was often written with long, beautiful melodies and accompaniments that rely on the use of the pedal for legato. Composers wrote especially for the sound of the piano. They were inspired by the improvements to the piano, and began to write music which highlighted its expressive range. Romantic piano pieces frequently have descriptive titles and are called *character pieces.* The *waltz* became a popular dance which replaced the *minuet.* The use of national folk music also became popular with the composers in the Romantic era.

Important Romantic composers:

Franz Schubert (Austria, 1797-1828)
Robert Schumann (Germany, 1810-1856)
Frédéric Chopin (b. Poland 1810 - d. France 1849)
Friedrich Burgmüller (b. Germany 1806 - d. France 1874)
Edvard Grieg (Norway, 1843-1907)

4. The 20th Century (1900 - 2000)

The 20th century was a time of great change in the world. Inventions such as the telephone, automobile, airplane, and computer set the 20th century apart from previous eras in a distinct way. These changes are reflected in the art, architecture, and music of the 20th century.

The piano of the 20th century is larger and more resonant than the pianos of the Romantic period. The modern grand piano has a brilliant tone necessary for projection in large concert halls. The second half of the 20th century saw the development of electronic pianos with digitally mastered sound.

Piano music of the 20th Century is written in many different styles. 20th century piano pieces are frequently written in forms made popular in previous eras. However, 20th century composers typically experimented with unusual harmonies, scales and rhythms to give their music a distinctly different sound than music of the earlier periods. In the first half of the 20th century several important new musical styles were *impressionism, atonal music,* and *jazz.* In the second half of the 20th century, electronic keyboards and synthesizers became an important part of creating new musical sounds. Also unique to the 20th century was the invention of sound recordings.

Important 20th Century composers:

Béla Bartók (b. Hungary 1881 - d. New York 1945)
Dmitri Kabalevsky (Russia, 1904-1987)
Dmitri Shostakovich (Russia, 1906-1975)
Aaron Copland (America, 1900-1990)
Sergei Prokofiev (Russia, 1891-1953)

Unit 14

Sight Reading

The best way to become a good sight reader is to read new music everyday.

1. Before you sight read, look through the entire piece and observe:
    - the key signature
    - the time signature
    - the clef signs
    - dynamics
    - accidentals
    - slurs, ties, staccatos, accents, etc.
    - rhythmic and melodic patterns
2. Find the first note and finger number for each hand.
3. Play slowly.
    - Use a metronome to keep a steady beat.
    - Count one measure aloud before you begin to play.
    - Continue to count aloud as you play.
4. Keep your eyes on the music.
    - Avoid looking up and down from the music to your hands.
    - Look ahead to see what is next.
5. Keep going, even if you make some mistakes.
    - Avoid going back to fix anything.

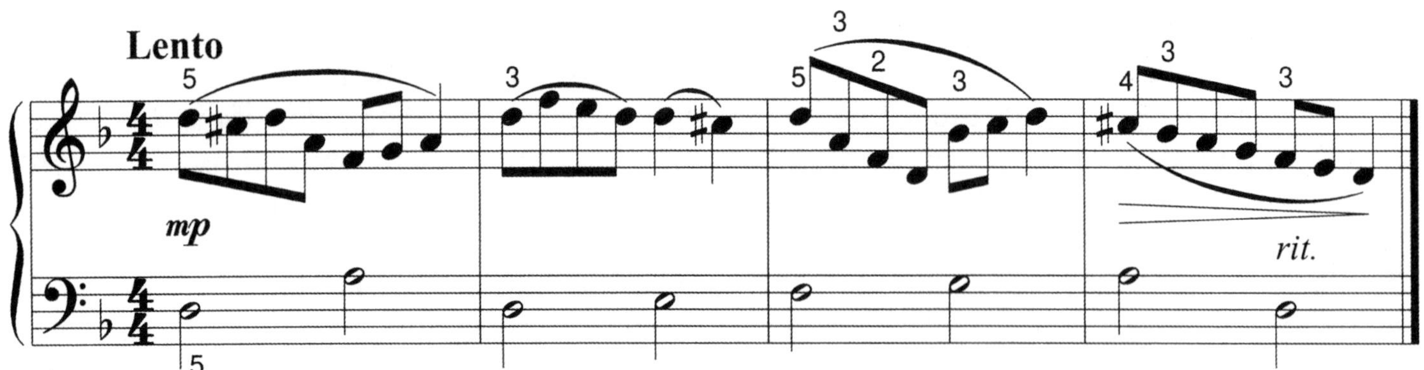

After you sight read:

1. Evaluate your playing.
    - Were the notes and rhythm correct?
    - Were the dynamics and articulation markings clear and distinct?
    - Did the music continue to move forward as you maintained a steady beat?
2. Sight read the music again.
    - Concentrate on correcting any previous mistakes.
    - Set a goal for a perfect performance by the third reading.

Allegretto
mp
f
mf
Spiritoso
mf
f
Adagio
p
mf
poco rit.

Unit 15

Ear Training

Practice # 1

Listen as your teacher plays one interval from each pair. Circle the one you hear.

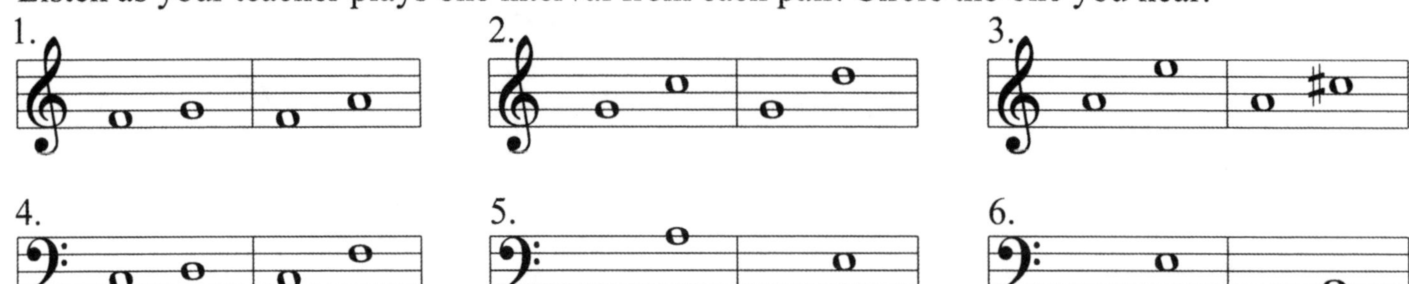

Listen as your teacher plays a Major or minor melody. Check (✓) the one you hear.

Listen as your teacher plays a Major or minor triad. Circle the one you hear.

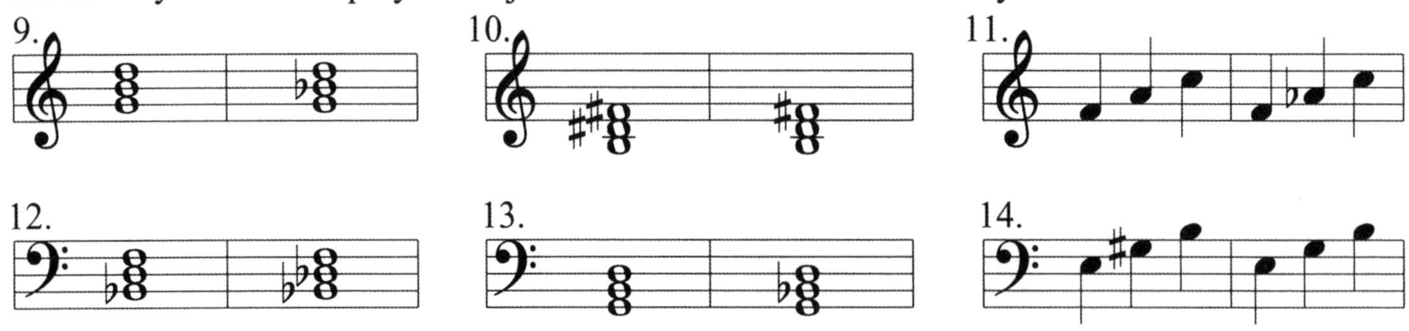

Listen as your teacher taps one rhythm from each pair. Check the one you hear.

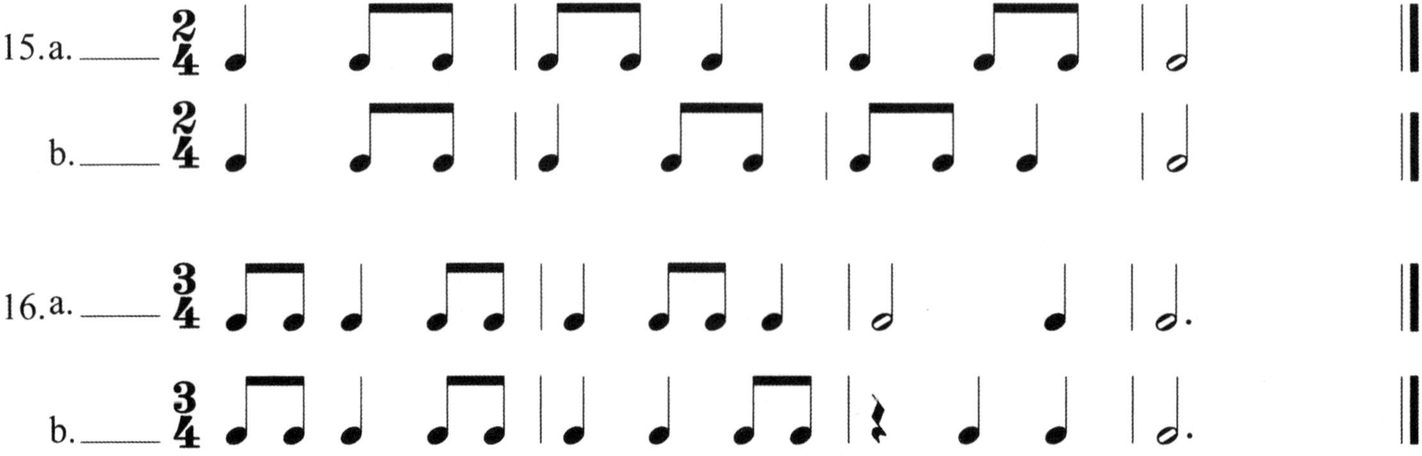

Practice # 2

Listen as your teacher plays one interval from each pair. Circle the one you hear.

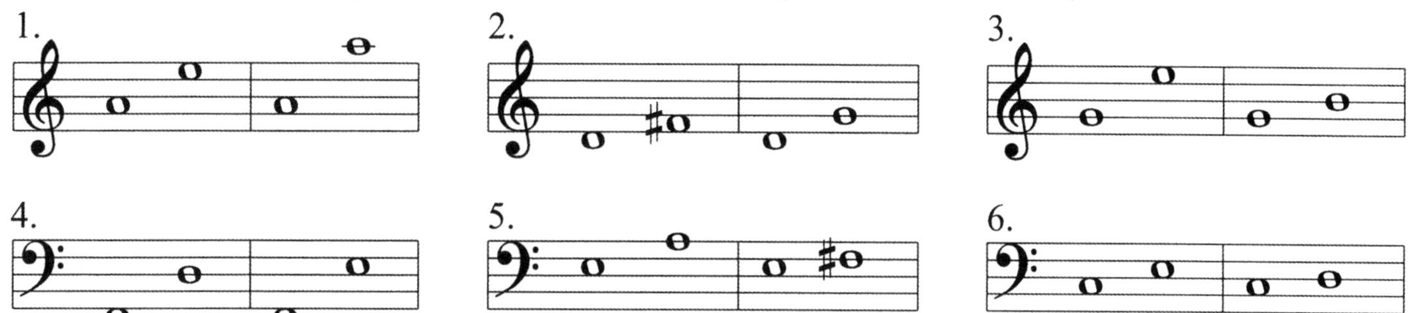

Listen as your teacher plays a Major or minor melody. Check (✓) the one you hear.

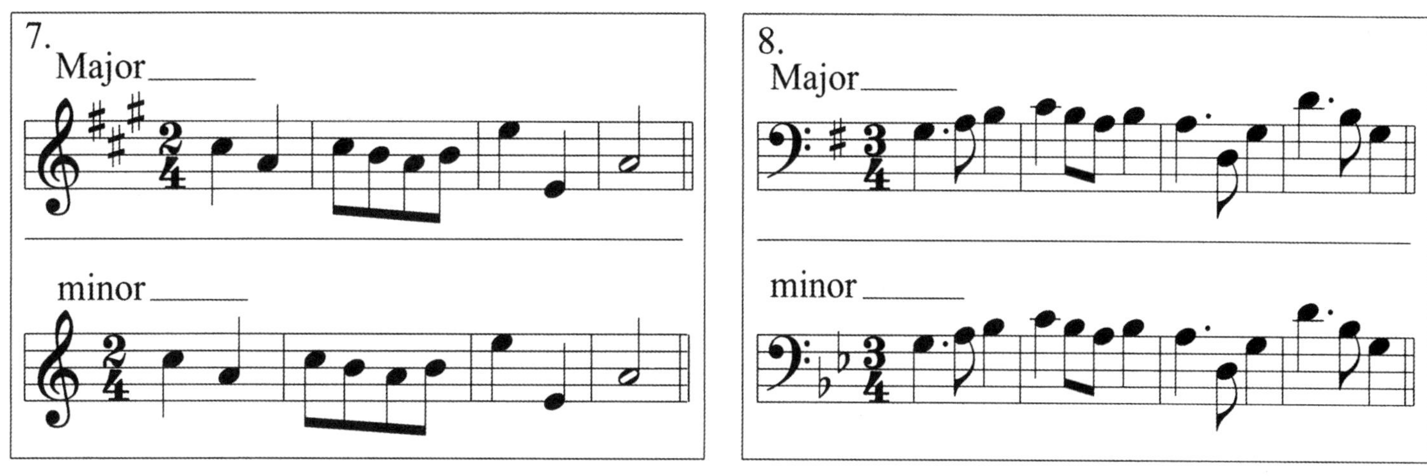

Listen as your teacher plays a Major or minor triad. Circle the one you hear.

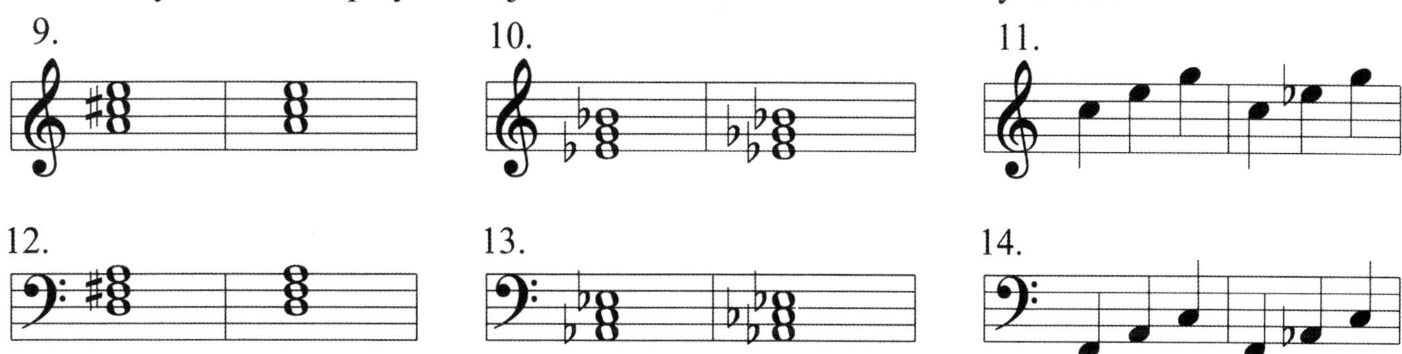

Listen as your teacher taps one rhythm from each pair. Check the one you hear.

Review Test

1. Name these Major key signatures.

2. Name these Minor key signatures.

3. Add the correct sharps or flats to form these scales.

A Major

B♭ Major

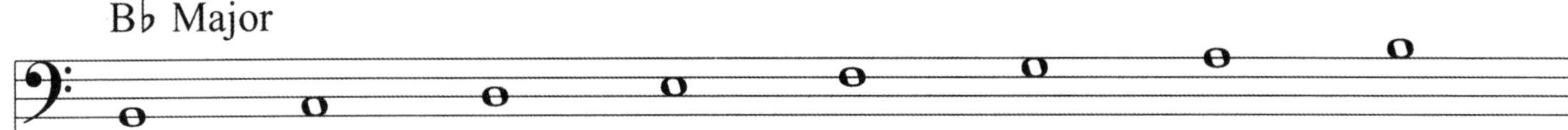

D harmonic minor

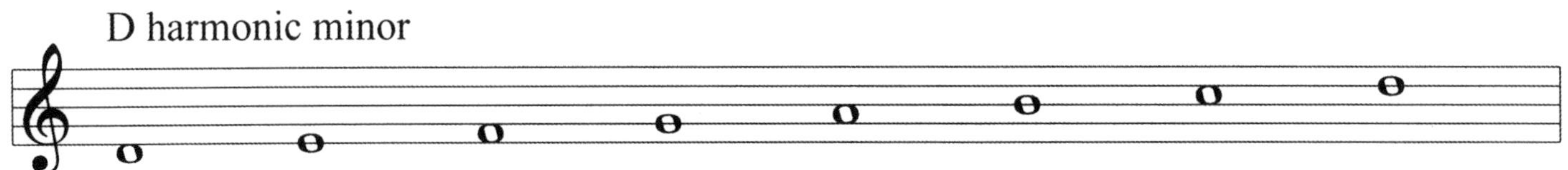

4. Name these intervals of the scale. Write **M** for Major and **P** for Perfect.

Key of ________

Key of ________

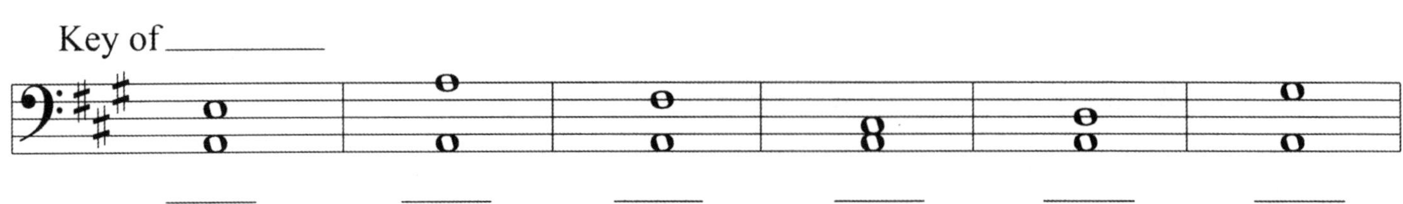

5. Name the root of each triad. Tell if it is Major or minor.

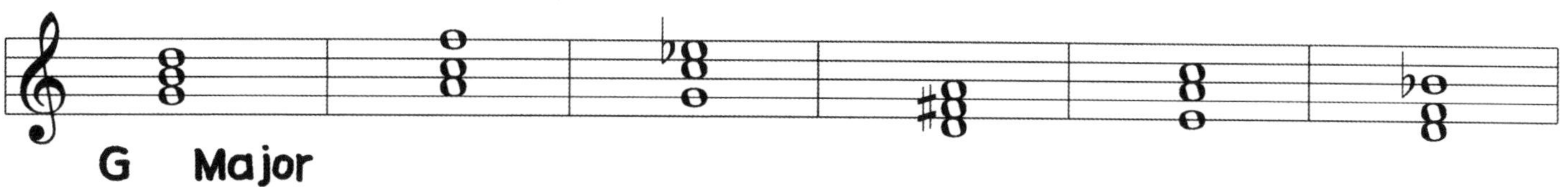

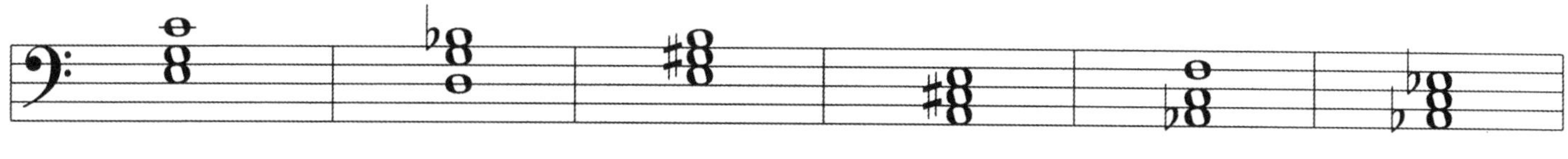

6. Draw an Augmented triad after each Major triad.

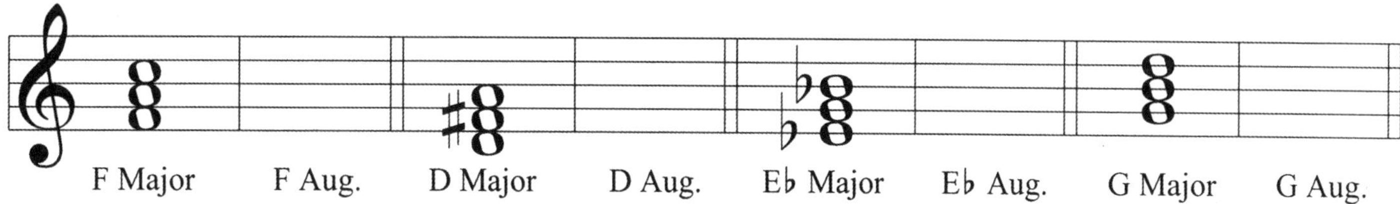

7. Draw a diminished triad after each minor triad.

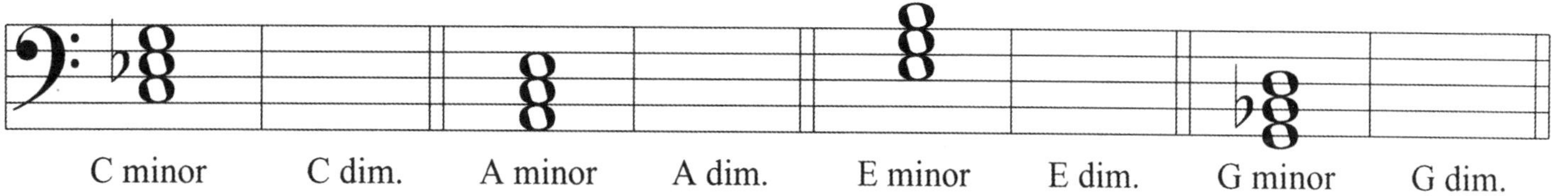

8. Write in the counts.

9. What is the relative minor to D Major? __________

10. What is the relative minor to G Major? __________

11. What is the relative minor to B♭ Major? __________

12. Study this *Minuet* to answer the question on page 63.
Measure numbers are placed at the beginning of each line for reference.

Minuet

BWV Anh. 132

From the
Notebook for Anna Magdalena Bach
(1725)

a. What is the meaning of *Andante* ? ______________

b. What is the key of this piece? ______________

c. What form of minor scale is used for the treble clef melody in measures 3 and 4?

____

d. Name the circled interval in measure 2. Tell if it is Major or Perfect. _______

e. Name the circled interval in measure 4. Tell if it is Major or Perfect. _______

f. Write in the counts in measure 7.

g. What triad is formed by the left hand notes in measure 7? ______________

h. Measure 9 has a repeat sign. Measure 9 and 10 have this sign over them:

1. 2.

:||

Explain what this means to do when playing this piece.

____

____

i. Look at the right hand notes in measures 10 and 11 and compare them to the right hand notes in measures 12 and 13. This is an example of (*circle your answer):*

sequence **repetition**

j. What form of minor scale is used in the right hand notes in measure 14?

____

k. What type of chord is formed by the circled bass clef notes in measures 14 and 15?

____

l. Write in the counts in measure 11.

m. What is the form of this piece (*circle your answer)?* **Binary** **Ternary**

n. What is the style of this music (*circle your answer)?* **Polyphonic** **Homophonic**

o. This piece was written during the (*circle your answer):*

Baroque period **Classical period**

13. Match these Roman numerals with their names.

I	____ dominant
IV	____ tonic
V	____ subdominant

15. Write the name for each cadence (authentic or half).

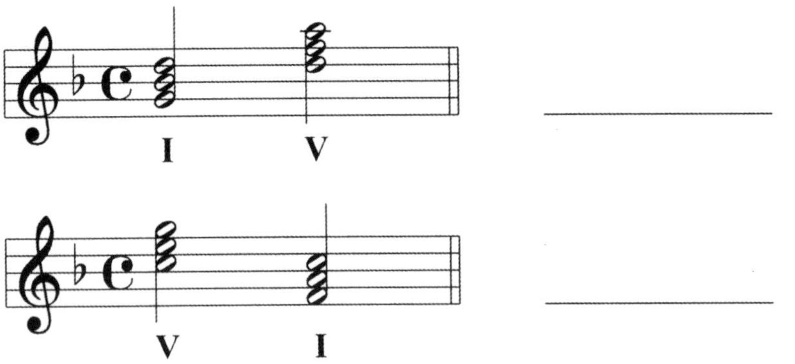

____

____

14. Match these signs and terms with their meanings.

A. adagio	____ much
B. accelerando	____ little
C. dolce	____ spirited
D. molto	____ gradually faster
E. *ppp*	____ $\frac{2}{2}$, alla breve
F. spiritoso	____ sweetly
G. poco	____ fast
H. ₵	____ slow
I. allegro	____ very, very soft

16. The music below uses primary chords for the left hand accompaniment. Label the chords with Roman numerals (I, IV, V, or V7).

17. Transpose the music above to B♭ Major.

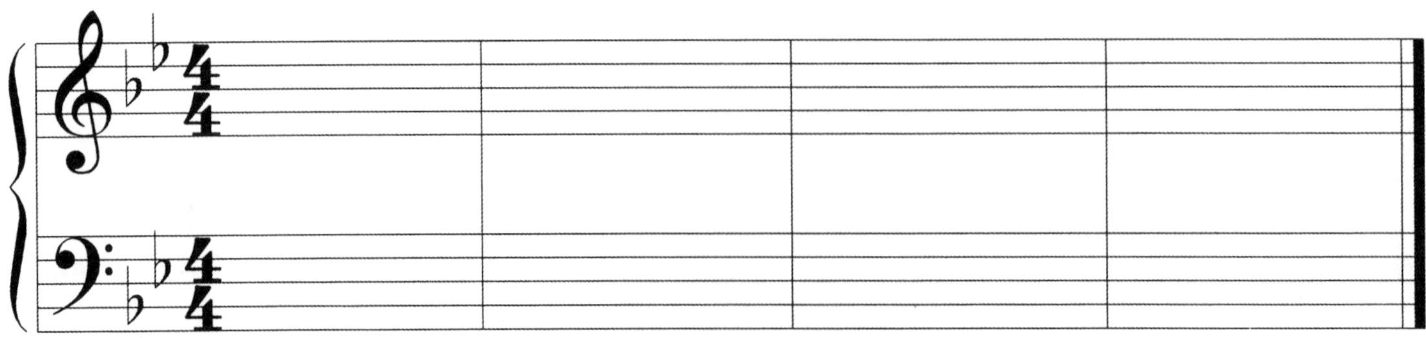